FOOT AND MOUTH DISEASE:
THE 1967 OUTBREAK AND ITS AFTERMATH

The transcript of a Witness Seminar held by the Wellcome Trust Centre for the History of Medicine at UCL, London, on 11 December 2001

Edited by L A Reynolds and E M Tansey

Volume 18 2003

CONTENTS

ILLUSTRATIONS AND CREDITS

INTRODUCTION

In December 2001 the History of Twentieth Century Medicine Group chose a veterinary disease for the subject of a Witness Seminar, the first time in its nine years' existence. Although the title specified the 1967–68 outbreak, it so happened that at that time Britain was still in the grip of its worst outbreak of foot and mouth disease (FMD) since 1967.

Epizootics, or plagues affecting domestic animals, have for centuries caused havoc in farming communities in every continent across the globe. FMD may be assumed to have appeared in higher mammals at the time when man began his first forays into animal husbandry and became dependent on herds of domestic animals, inevitably susceptible to diseases of various kinds. Their presence is documented in descriptions in early Graeco–Roman literature from Aristotle (384–322 BCE) and the elder Pliny (CE 24–79) to Vegetius (*fl.c.* CE 450), although retrospective diagnosis must always be treated with caution. Confusion between FMD and rinderpest (cattle plague), both viral diseases and highly infectious, continued well into the nineteenth century.[1] As indicated by its suffix 'plague', the latter disease is far more deadly than FMD, with a fatality rate of up to 1 in 10 animals per affected herd.

That Britain's position as an island offered some protection against the introduction of animal diseases from its continental neighbours was described as early as 1807 by Samuel Bardsley (1764–1851), physician to the Manchester Infirmary.[2] George Fleming (1833–1901), veterinary inspector to the War Office and later to the Army, noted 30 years later that in 1839 '...our ports were thrown open to foreign cattle',[3] and rinderpest, FMD, and contagious pleuropneumonia of cattle were introduced to a country whose veterinary profession was not well prepared to deal with epizootics in domestic animals in general. Most veterinary surgeons had been educated at the London Veterinary College, under Edward Coleman (1765–1839), that animal medicine was inferior to its human counterpart, and that horses were worth exclusive attention compared to other domestic animals.

---

[1] Wilkinson (1992): chapters 1 and 2.

[2] ibid., 82. S A Bardsley also published on rabies in the *Memoirs of the Literary and Philosophical Society of Manchester.*

[3] Fleming (1871): xxxiv.

By the end of the 1860s, after the rinderpest epidemic, the responsibility for increasingly tighter controls on imports from countries harbouring infections with cattle diseases finally passed to the state. After very serious outbreaks in 1871 affected an estimated 3 million animals, the sheer scale of that epidemic led to the inclusion of FMD as notifiable under the Contagious Diseases (Animals) Act (1869).[4] The economic burden was high. To quote again George Fleming, writing in 1871 after the 1865–66 outbreak of rinderpest:

> The losses from only two exotic bovine maladies ('contagious pleuropneumonia' and the so-called 'foot and mouth disease') have been estimated to amount ...to 5 549 780 head, roughly valued at £83 616 854.[5]

In Britain the emphasis was on isolation of infected animals and their possible contacts; prevention of movement of livestock within infected areas; and consequent closure of markets and fairs; measures which were successful in banishing endemic FMD from Britain by the end of 1884.[6]

By the later decades of the nineteenth century, increased microbiological knowledge paved the way for the emergence of the new discipline of bacteriology. Discovery of the existence, if not yet the structure and the nature of 'filterable viruses' additionally facilitated diagnostic characterization. Early work on vaccines followed Koch's work on anthrax and Pasteur's on rabies; work which was to develop in the twentieth century to benefit the fight against animal diseases as well as human ones.[7]

With regard to FMD vaccines in Britain, it is curious that although state-sponsored research followed the serious outbreaks in 1922 and 1924 at the Pirbright Institute,[8] the resultant effective vaccines have never been used in outbreaks in Britain. Even now, into the twenty-first century, the exclusive use of slaughter continues to find favour, as demonstrated in the most recent, severe outbreaks in 2001–02. Yet the Pirbright Animal Virus Research Institute has long been recognized as the World Reference Laboratory, with samples submitted from countries worldwide, and offering information, published annually, in return.[9]

---

[4] See note 6, page 4.

[5] Fleming (1871): xxxiv.

[6] See Henderson (1954): 91.

[7] Fleming (1871): xxxiv.

[8] See note 8, page 5.

[9] For details of the work of the World Reference Laboratory, see Brooksby (1974): 20–21.

The work at Pirbright had been preceded in this country by important work on pleuropneumonia and FMD at the Brown Institution, established by the University of London in the 1870s.[10] By the 1920s, this work continued, with the benefit of better facilities and improvements in methodology at the Lister Institute. The Lister Institute's work on FMD was carried out during a period of threats of new outbreaks. For safety reasons the experiments took place on an obsolete warship moored off Harwich,[11] under the auspices of the Ministry of Agriculture. This work showed the possibility of transmission of FMD to guinea pigs and other small mammals, which in turn led to the realization of the danger of transmissibility of the disease within natural populations of hedgehogs, which could act as carriers over considerable distances. That possibility has been mentioned in discussions of sources on the spread of the disease in 1967 – perhaps as well in a country intent on preserving its populations of hedgehogs.[12]

In spite of all the important work done in the 1920s, by June 1926 the *British Medical Journal* warned that the country was still 'suffering from this very serious disease, which threatens to become enzootic', and stressed the 'utmost importance' of keeping the country free from the disease 'by scientific means':

> 'Britain is no longer an island, and it seems obvious that the pole-axe method cannot be indefinitely used to stamp out the disease. It has been fairly successful in the United States – but that country is a much more effective "island" than this country, and there is less danger of its reintroduction there.'[13]

We might add here that Professor Fred Brown FRS, who spent most of his working life in Britain, but unfortunately could not attend our Witness Seminar because of other commitments, is currently working at the US Department of Agriculture's Plum Island Animal Disease Centre, NY.[14] During the 2001 FMD crisis he was interviewed by the British Broadcasting Corporation (BBC); while making no reference to our relatively protected position as an island, as first

---

[10] See Wilkinson (1992): chapter 10.

[11] Chick *et al.* (1971): 1135–1136.

[12] See Northumberland (1969a): 114.

[13] Anon. (1926): 1002.

[14] See Biographical notes on page 85.

noted almost two centuries earlier by Bardsley,[15] he did pronounce himself entirely in favour of a combined slaughter plus vaccination policy.[16]

Progress in the experimental work at Pirbright is reflected in its first five reports from 1925 to 1937, when each report lists laboratory alterations and improvements, matching increasing knowledge of virus diseases in general and of FMD in particular. Also all experimental areas had improved safety measures including 'vermin-proof' fencing, carcass incinerators, and manure destructors. Meanwhile the research work at other centres was gradually discontinued; and in 1939, the last such laboratories at the National Institute for Medical Research (NIMR), at Hampstead, were closed. From then on the Pirbright Institute expanded its laboratories and experimental units as the only centre for work on FMD in the UK.[17]

A severe postwar FMD outbreak in 1952 coincidentally saw the beginnings of another major expansion to increase facilities at Pirbright for virus research in the fields added in the 1950s and 1960s, such as research on pathology and genetics, using tissue culture. However, in spite of additional work on exotic viruses, Pirbright still had no provision for filtration of outgoing air. Only after that outbreak were filtration plants installed in all experimental cattle units.[18]

The 1952–53 outbreak was as severe as those in the 1920s, and was described in detail in the first of the new postwar Committee of Inquiry *Reports* to the Ministry of Agriculture. This became known as the 'Gowers' Report after its chairman, Sir Ernest Gowers,[19] and was addressed to the Rt Hon. Sir Thomas

---

[15] See note 2 above.

[16] Professor Fred Brown wrote: 'I consider that the FMD Witness Seminar was a worthwhile exercise, timed as it was in the wake of the devastating outbreak of the disease in the UK in 2001. Although I was a member of the staff at Pirbright in 1967–68, not being a veterinarian, I was only on the fringe of what was going on in the field. Nevertheless I learned a lot about the larger world by talking to colleagues such as Drs Brooksby, Sellers and Mowat. Several clear messages emerged during the 1967–68 outbreak: (1) the role of sheep as a reservoir for the virus; (2) the presence of virus in the milk of cattle before they showed any clinical signs of the disease; (3) the importance of keeping animal movement to a minimum; (4) the logic of not importing products from FMD-infected countries. So why did the 2001 outbreak get out of control? It was largely because the lessons learned in the 1967–68 outbreak were ignored. A major recommendation of the Northumberland Report was to introduce ring vaccination if the disease got out of control. This should have been introduced in 2001.' Fax to Mrs Lois Reynolds, 25 August 2003.

[17] See Brooksby (1974): 16–17.

[18] See notes 71 and 72, page 51. See also ibid., 18–19.

[19] See biographical note on page 87.

Dugdale, the Minister of Agriculture and Fisheries. Their recommendations stress the necessity for 'energetic and rigorous measures' to prevent FMD becoming endemic in this country and hence causing a 'national calamity'. In spite of all the well-meaning precautions – of the implementation of devastating slaughter policies and of advice from expert committees and the Ministry concerned – the two later major epidemics, although not causing lasting endemicity, have fallen not far short of becoming calamities.[20]

In the present volume the 1967–68 FMD outbreak and its effects on the community are discussed by the professionals who were involved in its control and the efforts which eventually brought it to a close.

Lise Wilkinson

Wellcome Trust Centre for the History of Medicine at UCL

[20] See Gowers (1954): Chapter 6, and Northumberland (1969a, 1969b).

ACKNOWLEDGEMENTS

'Foot and Mouth Disease: The 1967 outbreak and its aftermath' was agreed as a suitable topic for a Witness Seminar by the Programme Committee. Ms Abigail Woods and Dr David Aicken suggested individuals to be invited, assisted Dr Daphne Christie plan the meeting, and helped to decide the topics to be discussed. We are very grateful to them for their input. We thank Dr Lise Wilkinson for her Introduction to these published proceedings. We are equally grateful to Lord Soulsby for his excellent chairing of the occasion. Our particular thanks go to Professor Fred Brown, for reading an earlier draft of the transcript. For additional help, we thank Miss Mary Brancker, Mr Keith Meldrum, Dr Noel Mowat, Mr Howard Rees, Dr Bob Sellers, Lord Soulsby, Mr Angus Taylor, and Dr Abigail Woods, who were also witnesses. Mr Allan Black of the Biotechnology and Biological Sciences Research Council Secretariat, Mr Nigel Chell of J C Bamford Excavators Ltd., Mr Nicholas Coney of The National Archives (Public Record Office), Kew, Mrs Margaret Ferre of HMSO-Norwich, Ms Pam Greening of the Royal College of Veterinary Surgeons Library and Information Service, Mr Steve Jebson of the National Meteorological Library and Archive, and Dr Sahra Gibbon all provided additional assistance with the text and illustrations.

We depend a great deal on our colleagues at the Wellcome Trust to ensure the smooth running of these meetings: the Audiovisual Department, and the Medical Photographic Library and Mrs Tracy Tillotson of the Wellcome Library; Ms Julie Wood, who has supervised the design and production of this volume; our indexer, Ms Liza Furnival; and our readers, Ms Lucy Moore and Mr Simon Reynolds. Mrs Jaqui Carter is our transcriber, and Mrs Wendy Kutner and Dr Daphne Christie assist us in running the meetings. Finally we thank the Wellcome Trust for supporting this programme.

Tilli Tansey

Lois Reynolds

Wellcome Trust Centre for the History of Medicine at UCL

WITNESS SEMINARS: MEETINGS AND PUBLICATIONS[1]

In 1990 the Wellcome Trust created a History of Twentieth Century Medicine Group, as part of the Academic Unit of the Wellcome Institute for the History of Medicine, to bring together clinicians, scientists, historians and others interested in contemporary medical history. Among a number of other initiatives the format of Witness Seminars, used by the Institute of Contemporary British History to address issues of recent political history, was adopted, to promote interaction between these different groups, to emphasize the potential of working jointly, and to encourage the creation and deposit of archival sources for present and future use. In June 1999 the Governors of the Wellcome Trust decided that it would be appropriate for the Academic Unit to enjoy a more formal academic affiliation and turned the Unit into the Wellcome Trust Centre for the History of Medicine at University College London from 1 October 2000. The Wellcome Trust continues to fund the Witness Seminar programme via its support for the Centre.

The Witness Seminar is a particularly specialized form of oral history, where several people associated with a particular set of circumstances or events are invited to come together to discuss, debate, and agree or disagree about their memories. To date, the History of Twentieth Century Medicine Group has held over 30 such meetings, most of which have been published, as listed on pages xvii–xxiii.

Subjects for such meetings are usually proposed by, or through, members of the Programme Committee of the Group, and once an appropriate topic has been agreed, suitable participants are identified and invited. These inevitably lead to further contacts, and more suggestions of people to invite. As the organization of the meeting progresses, a flexible outline plan for the meeting is devised, usually with assistance from the meeting's chairman, and some participants are invited to 'set the ball rolling' on particular themes, by speaking for a short period of time to initiate and stimulate further discussion.

Each meeting is fully recorded, the tapes are transcribed and the unedited transcript is immediately sent to every participant. Each is asked to check their

---

[1] The following text also appears in the 'Introduction' to recent volumes of *Wellcome Witnesses to Twentieth Century Medicine* published by the Wellcome Trust and the Wellcome Trust Centre for the History of Medicine at University College London.

own contributions and to provide brief biographical details. The editors turn the transcript into readable text, and participants' minor corrections and comments are incorporated into that text, while biographical and bibliographical details are added as footnotes, as are more substantial comments and additional material provided by participants. The final scripts are then sent to every contributor, accompanied by forms assigning copyright to the Wellcome Trust. Copies of all additional correspondence received during the editorial process are deposited with the records of each meeting in Archives and Manuscripts, Wellcome Library, London.

As with all our meetings, we hope that even if the precise details of some of the technical sections are not clear to the nonspecialist, the sense and significance of the events are understandable. Our aim is for the volumes that emerge from these meetings to inform those with a general interest in the history of modern medicine and medical science; to provide historians with new insights, fresh material for study, and further themes for research; and to emphasize to the participants that events of the recent past, of their own working lives, are of proper and necessary concern to historians.

Members of the Programme Committee of the History of Twentieth Century Medicine Group

The Group's activities are overseen by the Programme Committee, which includes professional historians of medicine, practising scientists and clinicians. The Programme Committee during 2002–03 comprised:

Dr Tilli Tansey – Historian of Modern Medical Science, Wellcome Trust Centre at UCL, and Chair

Sir Christopher Booth – Wellcome Trust Centre at UCL, former Director, Clinical Research Centre, Northwick Park Hospital, London

Dr Robert Bud – Head of Life and Environmental Sciences, Science Museum, London

Dr Daphne Christie – Senior Research Assistant, Wellcome Trust Centre at UCL, and Organizing Secretary

Professor Hal Cook – Director, Wellcome Trust Centre at UCL

Dr Mark Jackson – Reader, Centre for Medical History, Exeter

Professor Ian McDonald – Harveian Librarian, Royal College of Physicians, London

Dr Jon Turney – Head of the Department of Science and Technology Studies, University College London

HISTORY OF TWENTIETH CENTURY MEDICINE WITNESS SEMINARS, 1993–2003

1993 **Monoclonal antibodies**
Organizers: Dr E M Tansey and Dr Peter Catterall

1994 **The early history of renal transplantation**
Organizer: Dr Stephen Lock

Pneumoconiosis of coal workers
Organizer: Dr E M Tansey

1995 **Self and non-self: a history of autoimmunity**
Organizers: Sir Christopher Booth and Dr E M Tansey

Ashes to ashes: the history of smoking and health
Organizers: Dr Stephen Lock and Dr E M Tansey

Oral contraceptives
Organizers: Dr Lara Marks and Dr E M Tansey

Endogenous opiates
Organizer: Dr E M Tansey

1996 **Committee on Safety of Drugs**
Organizers: Dr Stephen Lock and Dr E M Tansey

Making the body more transparent: the impact of nuclear magnetic resonance and magnetic resonance imaging
Organizer: Sir Christopher Booth

1997 **Research in General Practice**
Organizers: Dr Ian Tait and Dr E M Tansey

Drugs in psychiatric practice
Organizers: Dr David Healy and Dr E M Tansey

The MRC Common Cold Unit
Organizers: Dr David Tyrrell and Dr E M Tansey

The first heart transplant in the UK
Organizer: Professor Tom Treasure

1998	**Haemophilia: recent history of clinical management** Organizers: Professor Christine Lee and Dr E M Tansey
	Obstetric ultrasound: historical perspectives Organizers: Dr Malcolm Nicolson, Mr John Fleming and Dr E M Tansey
	Post penicillin antibiotics Organizers: Dr Robert Bud and Dr E M Tansey
	Clinical research in Britain, 1950–1980 Organizers: Dr David Gordon and Dr E M Tansey
1999	**Intestinal absorption** Organizers: Sir Christopher Booth and Dr E M Tansey
	The MRC Epidemiology Unit (South Wales) Organizers: Dr Andy Ness and Dr E M Tansey
	Neonatal intensive care Organizers: Professor Osmund Reynolds and Dr E M Tansey
	British contributions to medicine in Africa after the Second World War Organizers: Dr Mary Dobson, Dr Maureen Malowany, Dr Gordon Cook and Dr E M Tansey
2000	**Childhood asthma, and beyond** Organizers: Dr Chris O'Callaghan and Dr Daphne Christie
	Peptic ulcer: rise and fall Organizers: Sir Christopher Booth, Professor Roy Pounder and Dr E M Tansey
	Maternal care Organizers: Dr Irvine Loudon and Dr Daphne Christie
2001	**Leukaemia** Organizers: Professor Sir David Weatherall, Professor John Goldman, Sir Christopher Booth and Dr Daphne Christie
	The MRC Applied Psychology Unit Organizers: Dr Geoff Bunn and Dr Daphne Christie
	Genetic testing Organizers: Professor Doris Zallen and Dr Daphne Christie

Foot and mouth disease: the 1967 outbreak and its aftermath
Organizers: Dr Abigail Woods, Dr Daphne Christie and Dr David Aickin

2002 **Environmental toxicology: the legacy of *Silent Spring***
Organizers: Dr Robert Flanagan and Dr Daphne Christie

Cystic fibrosis
Organizers: Dr James Littlewood and Dr Daphne Christie

Innovation in pain management
Organizers: Professor David Clark and Dr Daphne Christie

2003 **Thrombolysis**
Organizers: Mr Robert Arnott and Dr Daphne Christie

Beyond the asylum: anti-psychiatry and care in the community
Organizers: Dr Mark Jackson and Dr Daphne Christie

The Rhesus factor story
Organizers: Professor Doris Zallen and Dr Daphne Christie

PUBLISHED MEETINGS

"...Few books are so intellectually stimulating or uplifting".
Journal of the Royal Society of Medicine (1999) **92**: 206–208
review of vols 1 and 2

"...This is oral history at its best...all the volumes make compulsive reading...they are, primarily, important historical records".
British Medical Journal (2002) **325**: 1119 review of the series

Technology transfer in Britain: The case of monoclonal antibodies
Self and non-self: A history of autoimmunity
Endogenous opiates
The Committee on Safety of Drugs
In: Tansey E M, Catterall P P, Christie D A, Willhoft S V, Reynolds L A. (eds) (1997) *Wellcome Witnesses to Twentieth Century Medicine.* Volume 1. London: The Wellcome Trust, 135pp. ISBN 1 869835 79 4

Making the human body transparent: The impact of NMR and MRI
Research in General Practice
Drugs in psychiatric practice
The MRC Common Cold Unit
In: Tansey E M, Christie D A, Reynolds L A. (eds) (1998) *Wellcome Witnesses to Twentieth Century Medicine.* Volume 2. London: The Wellcome Trust, 282pp. ISBN 1 869835 39 5

Early heart transplant surgery in the UK
In: Tansey E M, Reynolds L A. (eds) (1999) *Wellcome Witnesses to Twentieth Century Medicine.* Volume 3. London: The Wellcome Trust, 72pp. ISBN 1 841290 07 6

Haemophilia: Recent history of clinical management
In: Tansey E M, Christie D A. (eds) (1999) *Wellcome Witnesses to Twentieth Century Medicine.* Volume 4. London: The Wellcome Trust, 90pp. ISBN 1 841290 08 4

Looking at the unborn: Historical aspects of obstetric ultrasound
In: Tansey E M, Christie D A. (eds) (2000) *Wellcome Witnesses to Twentieth Century Medicine.* Volume 5. London: The Wellcome Trust, 80pp. ISBN 1 841290 11 4

Post penicillin antibiotics: From acceptance to resistance?
In: Tansey E M, Reynolds L A. (eds) (2000) *Wellcome Witnesses to Twentieth Century Medicine.* Volume 6. London: The Wellcome Trust, 71pp. ISBN 1 841290 12 2

Clinical research in Britain, 1950–1980
In: Reynolds L A, Tansey E M. (eds) (2000) *Wellcome Witnesses to Twentieth Century Medicine.* Volume 7. London: The Wellcome Trust, 74pp. ISBN 1 841290 16 5

Intestinal absorption
In: Christie D A, Tansey E M. (eds) (2000) *Wellcome Witnesses to Twentieth Century Medicine.* Volume 8. London: The Wellcome Trust, 81pp. ISBN 1 841290 17 3

Neonatal intensive care
In: Christie D A, Tansey E M. (eds) (2001) *Wellcome Witnesses to Twentieth Century Medicine.* Volume 9. London: The Wellcome Trust Centre for the History of Medicine at UCL, 84pp. ISBN 0 854840 76 1

British contributions to medical research and education in Africa after the Second World War
In: Reynolds L A, Tansey E M. (eds) (2001) *Wellcome Witnesses to Twentieth Century Medicine.* Volume 10. London: The Wellcome Trust Centre for the History of Medicine at UCL, 93pp. ISBN 0 854840 77 X

Childhood asthma and beyond
In: Reynolds L A, Tansey E M. (eds) (2001) *Wellcome Witnesses to Twentieth Century Medicine.* Volume 11. London: The Wellcome Trust Centre for the History of Medicine at UCL, 74pp. ISBN 0 854840 78 8

Maternal care
In: Christie D A, Tansey E M. (eds) (2001) *Wellcome Witnesses to Twentieth Century Medicine.* Volume 12. London: The Wellcome Trust Centre for the History of Medicine at UCL, 88pp. ISBN 0 854840 79 6

Population-based research in south Wales: The MRC Pneumoconiosis Research Unit and the MRC Epidemiology Unit
In: Ness A R, Reynolds L A, Tansey E M. (eds) (2002) *Wellcome Witnesses to Twentieth Century Medicine.* Volume 13. London: The Wellcome Trust Centre for the History of Medicine at UCL, 74pp. ISBN 0 854840 81 8

Peptic ulcer: Rise and fall
In: Christie D A, Tansey E M. (eds) (2002) *Wellcome Witnesses to Twentieth Century Medicine.* Volume 14. London: The Wellcome Trust Centre for the History of Medicine at UCL, 143pp. ISBN 0 854840 84 2

Leukaemia
In: Christie D A, Tansey E M. (eds) (2003) *Wellcome Witnesses to Twentieth Century Medicine.* Volume 15. London: The Wellcome Trust Centre for the History of Medicine at UCL, 86pp. ISBN 0 85484 087 7

The MRC Applied Psychology Unit
In: Reynolds L A, Tansey E M. (eds) (2003) *Wellcome Witnesses to Twentieth Century Medicine.* Volume 16. London: The Wellcome Trust Centre for the History of Medicine at UCL, 94pp. ISBN 0 85484 088 5

Genetic testing
In: Christie D A, Tansey E M. (eds) (2003) *Wellcome Witnesses to Twentieth Century Medicine.* Volume 17. London: The Wellcome Trust Centre for the History of Medicine at UCL, 130pp. ISBN 0 85484 094 X

Foot and mouth disease: The 1967 outbreak and its aftermath
In: Reynolds L A, Tansey E M. (eds) (2003) *Wellcome Witnesses to Twentieth Century Medicine.* Volume 18. London: The Wellcome Trust Centre for the History of Medicine at UCL, 114pp. ISBN 0 85484 096 6

Environmental toxicology: The legacy of *Silent Spring*
In: Christie D A, Tansey E M. (eds) (2004) *Wellcome Witnesses to Twentieth Century Medicine.* Volume 19. London: The Wellcome Trust Centre for the History of Medicine at UCL, in press. ISBN 0 85484 091 5

Cystic fibrosis
In: Christie D A, Tansey E M. (eds) (2004) *Wellcome Witnesses to Twentieth Century Medicine.* Volume 20. London: The Wellcome Trust Centre for the History of Medicine at UCL, in press. ISBN 0 85484 086 9

Volumes 1–12 cost £5.00 plus postage, with volumes 13–18 at £10 each. Orders of four or more volumes receive a 20 per cent discount. All 18 published volumes in the series are available at the special price of £95 plus postage. To order a copy contact t.tillotson@wellcome.ac.uk or by phone: +44 (0)20 7611 8486; or fax: +44 (0)20 7611 8703.

Other publications

Technology transfer in Britain: The case of monoclonal antibodies
In: Tansey E M, Catterall P P. (1993) *Contemporary Record* **9**: 409–444.

Monoclonal antibodies: A witness seminar on contemporary medical history
In: Tansey E M, Catterall P P. (1994) *Medical History* **38**: 322–327.

Chronic pulmonary disease in South Wales coalmines: An eye-witness account of the MRC surveys (1937–1942)
In: P D'Arcy Hart, edited and annotated by E M Tansey. (1998) *Social History of Medicine* **11**: 459–468.

Ashes to Ashes – The history of smoking and health
In: Lock S P, Reynolds L A, Tansey E M. (eds) (1998) Amsterdam: Rodopi BV, 228pp. ISBN 90420 0396 0 (Hfl 125) (hardback). Reprinted 2003.

Witnessing medical history. An interview with Dr Rosemary Biggs
In: Professor Christine Lee and Dr Charles Rizza. (interviewers) (1998) *Haemophilia* **4**: 769–777.

FOOT AND MOUTH DISEASE:
THE 1967 OUTBREAK AND ITS AFTERMATH

The transcript of a Witness Seminar held by the Wellcome Trust Centre for the History of Medicine at UCL, London, on 11 December 2001

Edited by L A Reynolds and E M Tansey

FOOT AND MOUTH DISEASE:
THE 1967 OUTBREAK AND ITS AFTERMATH

Participants

Dr Maurice Allen
Miss Mary Brancker
Professor Leslie Brent
Mr Gareth Davies
Dr Tony Garland
Professor Alan Glynn
Mr Sherwin Hall
Mr Keith Meldrum
The Duke of Montrose
Mr James Morris
Dr Noel Mowat
Dr Hugh Platt
Dr Walter Plowright
Lord Plumb
Mr Howard Rees
Dr Alan Richardson
Professor David Rowlands
Mr Chris Schermbrucker
Dr Bob Sellers
Lord Soulsby (Chair)
Dr Tilli Tansey
Mr Angus Taylor
Mr Ken Tyrrell
Ms Abigail Woods

Among those attending the meeting: Dr Derek Bangham, Dr John Beale, Dr Mary Cotes, Professor Leslie Collier, Mr David Lloyd, Mr Tom Roper, Dr Lise Wilkinson, Dr Sarah Wilmot

Apologies include: Sir Derek Andrews, Mr Roger Blamire, Professor Fred Brown, Professor Chris Bostock, Dr Alex Donaldson, Mr Norman Ellis, Sir Brian Follett, Mr John Gripper, Mr Donald Martin, Mr Leonard Napolitan, Mr Hubert Skinner, Mr Anthony John Stevens, Dr David Tyrrell, Dr David Rhys Williams

Dr Tilli Tansey: May I begin by welcoming you all to this meeting of the History of Twentieth Century Medicine Group, which was established in 1990 by the Wellcome Trust to bring together doctors, clinicians, scientists, historians, journalists, and others interested in the history of recent medicine and biomedical science. It devised a number of mechanisms to do that, one of which is this Witness Seminar format, where we invite people who have been involved in a particular event or discovery, to meet together, discuss and debate among themselves in a chairman-led discussion about what really happened. This meeting on foot and mouth disease (FMD) was organized by my colleagues, Dr Daphne Christie, Dr David Aickin and Ms Abigail Woods. We are delighted that so many of you have come here to share your experiences and reminiscences with us, and we are particularly delighted that Lord Soulsby has very generously offered to chair the meeting. And so without further ado, I will hand the meeting over to Lord Soulsby.

Lord Soulsby:[1] Thank you very much indeed. It is a great honour for me to chair this session, which I think will be very interesting indeed, because we have a number of people here who were very deeply involved in the 1967–68 outbreak. The Gowers Committee of 1954 reported among many observations that there had been no single year between 1929 and 1953 in which this country was completely free of FMD, though the outbreaks at that time were not of a major nature. But in October 1967 a major outbreak started in Bryn Farm, Oswestry, Shropshire, and that was traced to pig swill that contained infected Argentine lamb. There were more than 2000 reported cases of the disease over a nine-month period, and the slaughter of nearly half-a-million animals.[2] Thirty years later we have another outbreak where we have exceeded those figures.[3] We are concerned today with the historical aspects of the 1967 outbreak, and what happened at that time; we are here to explore veterinary, farming, scientific and political perspectives, and the implementation of these.

---

[1] For biographical information on participants and others, see the notes on pages 85–94.

[2] Great Britain relied on a slaughter policy for controlling FMD following the Contagious Diseases (Animals) Act 1892, which authorized and funded the Board of Agriculture and its successors to carry out compulsory slaughter of ruminant animals and swine affected by FMD. See Northumberland (1969b): 11.

[3] The last of 2364 cases was diagnosed on 4 June 1968. The cost to MAFF was around £370 million (in 2001 prices), including £280 million paid as compensation to farmers. The 2001 outbreak cost over £3 billion, including £1.2 billion paid to farmers. See Auditor General (2002): Appendix 2, Comparison with 1967–68 outbreak, 112.

Following the 1967 outbreak there was the Northumberland Report[4] of which Lord Plumb, for example, was a member. While we don't want to trespass on the present outbreak of FMD – and there may be occasions when I may have to stop you from doing that – nevertheless one is, of course, related to the other.

We have a lot of ground to cover and by my reckoning we should spend approximately 30 minutes on each topic area. May I request that when you do speak in the discussion that you give your name for the transcriber, so that we know who said what. You will be able to assess whether the transcript is an accurate record of what you said when it is sent to you. Please, when you do speak, try to keep it fairly brief and to the point. I am now going to ask for a historical introduction by Ms Woods, a veterinary surgeon and a graduate of Cambridge, who is doing a PhD on the history of FMD. So over to you, Ms Woods.

Ms Abigail Woods: I have been looking at the history of foot and mouth for about two-and-a-half years and I have to say this year's outbreak was quite a shock, because I thought my history had finished in 1968. I have gone back to the very beginning, 1839, when FMD was first recognized in Britain,[5] and chased the changing perceptions of, and responses to, the disease right up to the present day. As you probably know, FMD control first became the responsibility of the state in 1869, just after the cattle plague outbreak. Over the next 15 years, increasingly tight controls were placed on the import of livestock from infected nations, and measures at home were extended to enforce the isolation of infected animals and their contacts and to prevent the movement of livestock within designated infected areas. Veterinary officials then gained the power to close markets and fairs.[6] This is the framework of controls that is still in operation

---

[4] See Northumberland (1969a). The Duke of Northumberland chaired the committee appointed by Frederick Peart, Minister of Agriculture, Fisheries and Food, in February 1968. Members were Anthony Cripps, QC, Professor David Evans, C Henry Plumb, Eric Thomas, Sir Edward Thompson, Professor David Walker and Professor Sir William Weipers, with Mr John Jotcham as Secretary and Mrs Melba White as Assistant Secretary. See also note 2 and Woods (2004).

[5] FMD was first recognized in Britain in 1839 and the first statistical records show 27 254 cases during 1870. See MAFF (1968), based on MAFF (1965).

[6] The Contagious Diseases and Animals Act 1869 made FMD a notifiable disease and gave local authorities power to prohibit the movement of affected animals, and to appoint inspectors who could require premises be disinfected. An extension of that Act in 1878 required local authorities to employ veterinary inspectors, who could enter premises where they suspected the disease to exist. See MAFF (1968): 1–2. See also Blancou (2002); Brown (2003).

today. They succeeded in eliminating endemic FMD from Britain in 1884. Slaughter only became a common response in the early years of the twentieth century, when its application was gradually extended until it became the accepted policy of the Ministry of Agriculture (MAFF), and there have been no exceptions to slaughter since 1924. While vaccines have been in common use in parts of Europe and South America since the 1940s,[7] they have never been used in Britain, despite the substantial progress made in this department by researchers at Pirbright, where state-sponsored research began in 1926.[8] Until 1968 FMD was a frequent visitor. It usually entered either from Europe, where systematic attempts to control the disease had only really got going in the late 1950s and 1960s, or in Argentine meat. Most outbreaks were quite limited in scope and were rapidly stamped out under the direction of the Ministry of Agriculture, Fisheries and Food's (MAFF) veterinary inspectors. But on the handful of occasions extremely large epidemics occurred, 1922, 1924[9] and 1951 outbreak, which the Gowers inquiry looked into, and, of course, 1967.[10] Each of these massive epidemics has prompted the same sort of questions: Where did the disease come from? How can its future entry be prevented? Is the traditional policy for FMD control working, or should it be altered in some way? What factors assisted the spread of this disease, or prevented the rapid success of slaughter? Also accompanying every FMD outbreak is the human tragedy, where farmers see their life's work destroyed, and are confined to their homes for weeks. I hope today we are going to be able to explore some of these aspects of the 1967 outbreak, by learning of your experiences with and opinions about this disease.

Soulsby: Thank you very much for that brief outline. We will now go to the main part of the seminar, the first of which is the central response to the outbreak and Howard Rees will talk.

---

[7] See Glossary. See also Brown (2003); Vallée, *et al.* (1925); Frenkel (1947) and note 58.

[8] Dr Bob Sellers wrote: 'Pirbright Cattle Testing Station [Pirbright, Surrey] was made available for FMD in 1924 and the first experiments in cattle started on 2 May 1925. See Skinner (1989).' Note on draft manuscript, 15 August 2002. See also Glossary.

[9] See Pretyman (1922, 1925).

[10] Outbreaks of FMD in Europe declined between 1951 and 2000 as a result of vaccination in most areas (see Figure 12), as well as the application of effective sanitary measures and importation control. Vaccination of cattle against FMD within the European Union (EU) and most of continental Europe ceased by 1992. See notes 61, 62 and Figure 12. The Middle Eastern strains of FMD caused outbreaks later in Bulgaria, Italy, Greece and Turkey and were treated by slaughter, not vaccination. See www.aleffgroup.com/avisfmd/A010-fmd/mod0/0132-euro-his-geo.html (visited 13 May 2003), Gowers (1954); Kitching (1998).

Figure 1: Howard Rees, CB DVSM HonFRCVS, Chief Veterinary Officer, 1980–88.

Mr Howard Rees: Thank you, Chairman. I hope you will excuse me, but my memory of 34 years ago is a bit sparse in parts, but I will try my best and I am sure that people like Angus Taylor, who perhaps has got a better memory than I have, will correct me on some of the details.

As you all know, foot and mouth was not a new disease to us in 1967–68. Right through the 1950s and 1960s, it was not unusual to have outbreaks of FMD and sometimes we had two or three outbreaks in a year. The State Veterinary Service (SVS) as a whole was well prepared and trained to deal with FMD, so the response from head office would be to enact the procedures that were well practised over the years and had been successful. From 1954 to 1967, excluding the 1967–68 outbreak, we had had 1002 outbreaks, with an average of 75 cases every year, and there were only two years – 1963 and 1964 – when we were without the disease, the longest period without the disease since 1908. The SVS in those days was well practised in all the procedures that were required and we had a manual of instructions, which gave all the details of procedures that should be adopted, and after each outbreak if a new situation arose, then the instructions would be modified to take account of it. When the first case was diagnosed on 25 October 1967, the normal procedures were put into effect. Head office would set up its emergency team of veterinarians, and administrative support staff. When the disease was confirmed the infected area would be so designated by the admin staff and they would draw up the necessary legal instruments to enforce the standstill order.[11] In the field the control centres would be set up, this was all well drilled in the past as to where the centres should be, what they required etc, so the whole response was automatic in those days.

I have mentioned that between 1954 and 1967 there were 1002 cases, of which 179 were classified as primaries.[12] Now of these 179 primaries, over half never produced secondaries, so when the first case arrived in Oswestry, there was no reason to believe that it was going to explode into the epidemic it did, because we had experience of many incursions of the virus which didn't spread at all. Of these 179 primaries, 97 of them were attributed to imported meat, not only from Argentina, but from other South American countries, through swill, imported bones, meat, offal, meat wrappers, etc., and those 97 exclude the 1967–68 outbreak.

Source	Argentine meat	Other South American meat	Unknown origin	Total
Swill	18	12	14	44
Bones	13	12	5	30
Meat and offal	12	7	4	23
Total	43	31	23	97

Table 1: Origins of FMD outbreaks, 1954–67: 97 cases out of 179 primary outbreaks attributed to imported meat and meat wrappings.
See Northumberland (1969b), Table 10, 77.

Roughly 90 per cent of our primaries going right back to 1954 had been due to importations from South America. The response from the centre was to enact all the well-drilled procedures that had been used over the years and had been successful.

One of the complicating factors in this particular outbreak was that when it was diagnosed on 25 October, a Wednesday, the normal Oswestry market was taking

[11] The basic legislation for controlling FMD in Great Britain at the time was the Diseases of Animals Act, 1950, where Form C enforced a standstill or stop on all movements of susceptible animals. See Glossary and Northumberland (1969b): 11. For a description of the organization of veterinary staff, see The National Archives (PRO) MAF 287/512.

[12] See Glossary.

place, and when the disease was suspected Form C procedures were enacted,[13] which brings in the five miles emergency standstill order, and involved the market, just within the five miles. There were 3299 stock still left in the market, which were impounded there. Two cows from the original Ellis case[14] had gone to the market that morning. One had left the market and luckily the police were able to stop the vehicle and redirect it back to the farm, and the other was sent directly there. These two were examined the next day, 26 October, found free of the disease, but were included, of course, in the slaughter. It was decided that there would be no compulsory slaughter of all the stock in the market. The animals in the market were then dispersed within the infected area that had been declared in the meantime and a ten-mile standstill area imposed. If the recipient farms were outside that ten-mile area, the animals were sent to slaughterhouses[15] in the area. Some animals had left and gone as far as Banffshire in Scotland and to Devon in the south-west before Form C was enacted. All these animals were traced and found healthy, so the decision was taken not to introduce compulsory slaughter of all the animals in the market.

In retrospect I think a lot of people would say this was a very brave decision to take. No diseased animals came out of the market, although two animals from the infected farm had gone to the market that very morning. Once diagnosed on 25 October, the disease was discovered to have been present on the farm since 21 October. The decision not to slaughter was taken between head office and the Regional Veterinary Officer, Ernest Corrigall, who was a very strong character. That's the immediate background, Chairman, to the initial response.

Soulsby: May I just pose one or two questions before I open up the questioning? The first is to ask if you had any idea at the time how extensive the outbreak might become?

Rees: No, because we had no idea of the origin, the source of the infection, and we didn't know whether there were other affected farms in the area. This was a secondary concern, we didn't know whether this was a primary outbreak at that stage, so there was no idea as to how the disease would develop.

---

[13] Arrangements for controlling FMD before 1967–68 are listed in Northumberland (1969b): 11–22, and Appendix 2, 116–120.

[14] See Figure 3a–d, where the Ellis farm, near Nantmawr, Oswestry, Shropshire, is in the lower left corner.

[15] In 1967–68 there were more than 3000 slaughterhouses in the UK and 500 in 2001. See Auditor General (2002): Appendix 2, 11. See also figures for abattoirs in note 53.

May I go on, perhaps briefly, Chairman, to describe what happened after the disease was diagnosed on 25 October? On Saturday 28 October, there was a further case at a farm adjacent to Bryn Farm and on 29 October a further case was confirmed, again in close proximity to the original case, but these didn't give rise to concern at all. This was a normal pattern, it was just a very local spread. On Monday 30 October, the situation changed dramatically, when there were nine fresh cases confirmed, six close to the original outbreak. The other three represented big jumps of 12, 35 and 100 miles (the last in Carnforth, Lancashire), which did give us reason for concern, we knew we had something brewing. But until 30 October there was no reason to think that the number of cases was going to explode.

Soulsby: That opens the general discussion, we have about 20 minutes or so.

Professor Leslie Brent: I wonder whether a vaccine was available in 1967 and, if it was, whether its application was ever considered?

Rees: The answer, of course, is no. There were no Ministry vaccines available at that stage. Vaccine would have been available from manufacturers, but we did not have a vaccine bank then.[16]

Mr James Morris: I would like to point out that I arrived in the Oswestry centre from Pembrokeshire on Thursday morning, 26 October, and was sent out by the Divisional Veterinary Officer (DVO) to relieve the local veterinary officer who was there with the valuers at that time, following confirmation. The significance escaped me at the time, but the auctioneer, the farmer and the local veterinary officer were eating roast lamb. I am sure Howard Rees will explain the significance of that later on. I examined every animal at the time of slaughter and supervised burial, and there was no clinical evidence of disease in the cattle. The disease had been confined entirely to the pigs. The second case was in a farm across the road, which shared a weighing machine for the pigs with Ellis, so there was constant movement across the road and he was the next one to go down. So the disease at that stage, as far as Ellis was concerned, was apparently confined entirely to pigs and had not got into the cattle, which was fortunate in view of the Oswestry market.

Dr Bob Sellers: I just want to mention the Carnforth [Lancashire] outbreak, because when I was looking into outbreaks of FMD after the war, Bill Parkinson

---

[16] On 28 November 1967 MAFF made plans to stockpile vaccine and contingency plans were made for ring vaccination. See Northumberland (1969b): 73. See also note 20 and Glossary for details on the International Vaccine Bank. For contingency plans, see TNA(PRO) MAF 287/461 and for the discussion of future vaccination policy, see TNA(PRO) MAF 287/479/1.

told me a lot about the 1967 outbreak and what happened at Tolworth at that time.[17] The Carnforth outbreak was known as the John Kerr outbreak, as the field report came in at the same time as many others and John Kerr said, 'Let's take it' [confirm as FMD], and so they did.[18]

Soulsby: I am sure there will be more questions, but it does seem to me that 30 years, or more, ago the local livestock farming industry was quite different from today. Many of the markets were local and were probably held every week. One knew where all the animals came from and where they went after the market. Is that so, compared with the present outbreak where there were a very limited number of markets and animals went nationwide?

Rees: Yes, I think it is true that we knew their destinations then, as the auctioneers had to keep a record of where the animals had gone.[19] I have mentioned that they did travel long distances even then. Maybe they came into the market from local areas, but they could go to Scotland and down to the south-west. I forgot to mention earlier that the 1967 outbreak, which started in Oswestry in October, was the third outbreak that year. We had had one in January in Hampshire, which resulted in 29 cases, and then a further outbreak in Warwickshire in September, with four cases.

Professor David Rowlands: Could I just ask which species of animals were principally involved in the earlier sporadic outbreaks?

Mr Angus Taylor: It was very often in pigs, and often due to swill. Could I just correct one point that the Chairman mentioned? Swill was not fed in the original farm near Oswestry. The report said that sheep bones were found in the yard which the pigs had access to, and we discovered eventually that the butcher did sell Argentine meat. But we occasionally had outbreaks in sheep. I can remember diagnosing an outbreak in a farm in Hampshire, although we never discovered the origin. We had a lot of FMD in that particular year, 1957–58, which went right down from Hampshire to Gloucestershire, Dorset and Somerset.

Sellers: As far as it goes, that is quite right; a lot of them were pigs and cattle, but there was quite an extensive outbreak involving sheep in Northumberland in 1966.

---

[17] Tolworth, Surrey, was the headquarters of the SVS from 1945 to 2001.

[18] Dr Bob Sellers wrote: 'John Kerr was Assistant Chief Veterinary Officer (ACVO) and Bill Parkinson was Divisional Veterinary Officer (DVO) at Tolworth in 1967.' Note on draft transcript, 22 May 2003.

[19] This also applied during the 2001 outbreak.

Figure 2: Mr John Reid (1906–90) CB FRCVS DVSM, Chief Veterinary Officer, 1965–70.

Miss Mary Brancker: You asked about vaccination and I didn't hear the reply, but I do know that there were very detailed arrangements made, because the Chief Veterinary Officer [John Reid, Figure 2] and I [as President of the British Veterinary Association] made them, and of course they were there for emergency use,[20] and if there had been a certain number of outbreaks by a certain date, then the plan would go into action. We planned every detail exactly – where the vaccine would be put in every area, including how much the veterinary surgeons would be paid.

[20] Miss Mary Brancker wrote: 'The Chief Veterinary Officer phoned me on Sunday 28 November, and asked me to come to Tolworth early on Monday morning (29 November) for a private discussion. We spent two hours together and during that time we made detailed plans for ring vaccination in the event that a specified number of outbreaks had been reached by a certain date. I cannot remember either the date or the number of outbreaks. Bearing in mind the vaccination had to be completed in ten days, the question concerned the number of veterinary surgeons that would be required. We calculated the number of animals to be vaccinated, the number that could be examined and vaccinated in an hour and the number of hours of daylight available in December. These calculations gave us the number of veterinary surgeons required and I estimated that enough volunteers could be found and that the offers from abroad need not be taken up. Finally we agreed the rate of pay for them. I did not attend the meeting at Oswestry on 2 December 1967.' Note on draft transcript, 5 September 2002.

Rees: Taking up Mary's point, I think the question was whether we had a vaccine available at the outset? Well, there was no bank of vaccine available at the Ministry at that stage. Obviously manufacturers had vaccine. I know Mary took part in the meetings, but this was on 2 December when they started looking into the possibility of vaccination, and perhaps we can come back to this later.

Soulsby: Howard, from what you say, because of the continuing number of outbreaks over the years, despite the two years of freedom, you were in fact geared up for an outbreak, all ready to move when it occurred. Is that so?

Rees: Yes, but the scale of the outbreak stretched our resources. In the first seven days we had had 23 outbreaks, 14 in the Nantmawr area [Figure 3] and the others scattered around, but it was difficult at that stage to conclude that these were all secondaries. The second week there were 104 fresh cases, and new control centres were set up then in Crewe, Chester, Ellesmere, Stafford and Northwich, and the distribution of the disease began to take this pattern. The third week there were 215 cases, the fourth week had 385 cases; 600 of the cases up to that time were on the Cheshire plain, which had the highest density of dairy cattle in this country, and possibly in the world. The epidemic reached its peak of 490 cases in the fifth week and on Friday, 24 November, we had 81 cases in one day, which turned out to be the peak. Two days later we had 80 cases, but it started to decline. As Mary said, there was a meeting in Oswestry on the 2 December with the Regional Veterinary Officer and a group of private veterinarians, to develop plans for vaccination, if the need should arise. When the epidemic appeared to be declining, this was abandoned, and although the plans were made, and vaccine was purchased, the decision was made not to vaccinate.

Dr Noel Mowat: I worked at Pirbright at the time and I seem to remember that provisions were made for purchasing something in the order of 3 million doses of the Frenkel-type vaccine from France.[21] I think there were also additional supplies earmarked from one of the South American countries.[22] One of my duties was to check that the potency of the vaccine was satisfactory, and I am happy to say that it was. I do remember that the Ministry at the time was obviously plotting the daily number of outbreaks and it was gradually reaching

---

[21] For historical background see Brown (2003) and Sellers (1984). See also Vallée *et al.* (1925, 1926); Frenkel (1947) and note 16 for discussion of vaccination policy.

[22] Dr Bob Sellers wrote: 'The vaccine came from Coopers (owned by Wellcome) in Uruguay.' Note on draft transcript, 15 August 2002.

Figure 3a–b: Outbreaks of FMD during the first and second weeks, October – November 1967. See the bottom left corner which is the Ellis farm, near Nantmawr. See note 14.

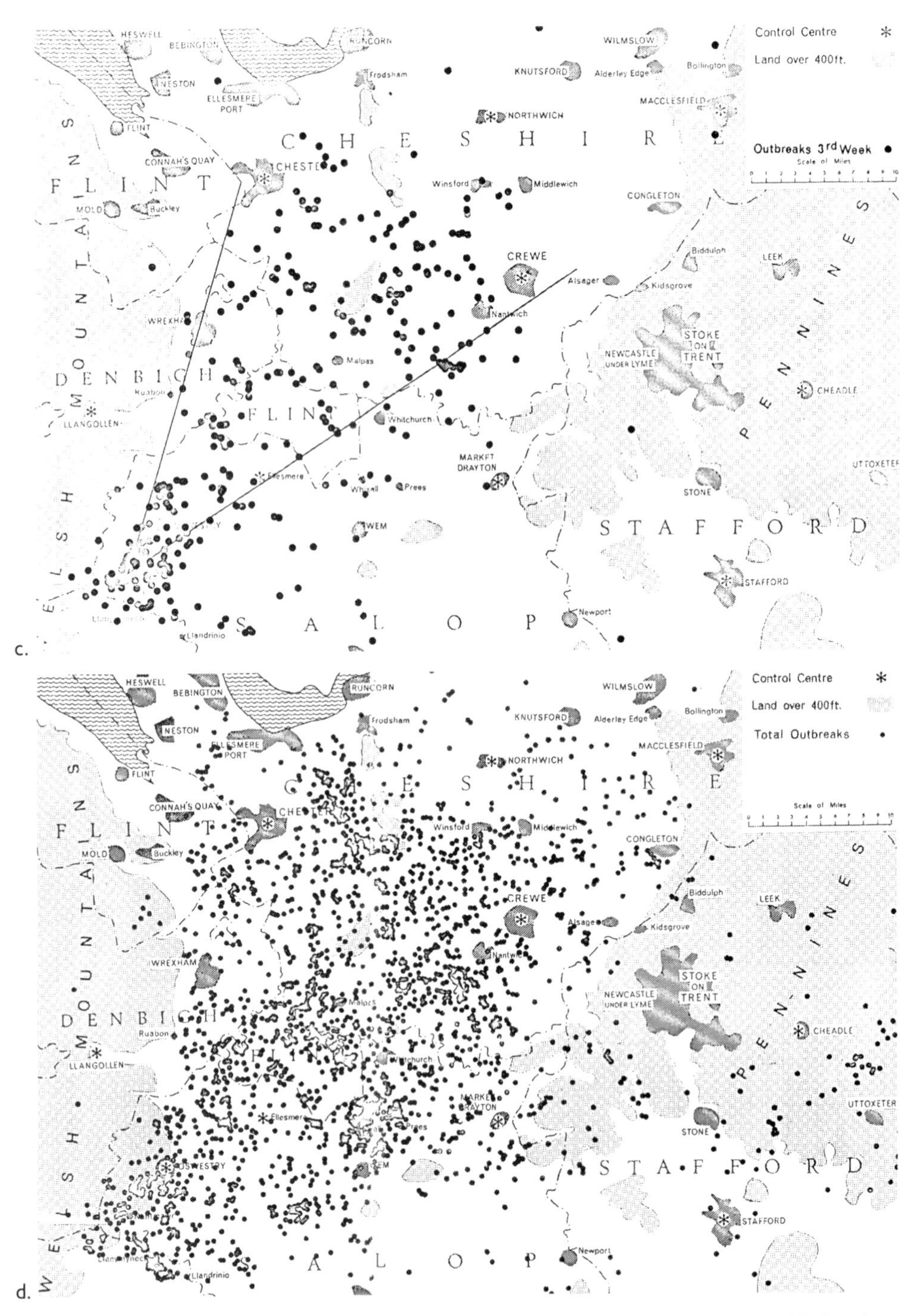

Figure 3c–d: Outbreaks of FMD during the third week and total outbreaks between 25 October 1967 and 4 June 1968. See note 14.

the peak. John Brooksby came to the conclusion that if the increase in cases continued for another day or two, then vaccination was inevitable. But the curve took a downward turn at that point and vaccination was not instituted.

Mr Sherwin Hall: In October 1967 I was in the Veterinary Investigation Centre, Wolverhampton. In mid-November when it was clear that the epidemic was beginning to spread, the laboratory staff were called out and I had to report to the Oswestry centre. By the end of November the Chief Veterinary Officer, John Reid, was concerned about how the FMD control centres and the normal reporting system were working. He gave me the task of getting the data on the history of the outbreak, with a view to having the details ready for the inquiry that would inevitably be held.[23] My problem was how to tackle it. It struck me that there was a variety of topics that seemed pertinent, and those were listed as subject headings, under which the evidence could be collected. The actual topic headings are listed below.

Armed with that sort of topic list, the interviews were all recorded on tape. Those tapes are not available now, but they were transcribed as 250 source sheets. The

---

Sherwin Hall's topic headings

1. Tolworth head office policy and technique
2. Weybridge Laboratory, Pirbright, and other laboratory services
3. Staff and accommodation
4. Valuation and compensation
5. Slaughter and immobilization
6. Carcass disposal and disinfection of infected premises (IPs)
7. Local authorities, police and fire services
8. Civilian contractors
9. Ministry of Defence and the Army
10. NFU, NUAW, CLA, RASE, WRVS
11. RSPCA
12. RCVS and the BVA
13. Milk Marketing Board and artificial insemination
14. Disruptions and consequential losses
15. Parliamentary, public and farming reaction
16. Press and information services
17. Supplies and equipment
18. Utility boards (gas, electricity and water) and the river authorities
19. Fatstock licensing, slaughterhouses and markets
20. Pest control
21. Animals
22. Origins of the epidemic and jumps; epidemiology
23. Insurance
24. Previous outbreaks in 1967

---

[23] See Reid (1968), reproduced in Northumberland (1969a): Appendix 3, 115–117. See also TNA(PRO) MAF 287/493.

Figure 4: Mr Keith Meldrum CB MRCVS DVSM HonFRSH, Chief Veterinary Officer, 1988–97.

first few of them recorded all of the details about the market at Oswestry that Howard Rees has alluded to and the difficulties facing Ernest Corrigall. I can remember at the time the MP for Oswestry wanted to raise a question in Parliament, but the Speaker apparently wouldn't accept it and so he wrote a letter to the Minister of Agriculture instead. Presumably all those notes should be in the Public Record Office [The National Archives (PRO), Kew, since April 2003].

Mr Keith Meldrum: At the time I was a veterinary officer working in both Northumberland and Hampshire, and later on in Crewe.

Howard, can you tell us how the disease was confirmed at the time? Did it have to relate to positive laboratory confirmation, such as virus isolation, or could it be done without? I remember later on, as you will, in 1972, that we confirmed FMD in pigs, which actually was swine vesicular disease (SVD), based simply on clinical grounds. Was that the norm?

Secondly, in passing, the outbreak in Hampshire was particularly interesting historically, because, of course, that was disease in a slaughterhouse lairage[24] and it had very close similarities to the problems we have had this year. The first case in 2001 was diagnosed in Cheale's slaughterhouse in Essex,[25] where they brought in swill-fed pigs; and the same applied in Funtley abbatoir in Hampshire, where pigs were kept far too long and went down [with the disease] due to lairage contamination with the virus.

Rees: Returning to your question about the initial case. Normally, in those days, confirmation for the first case was usually on the basis of laboratory diagnosis, to ensure that we had FMD virus. Thereafter, diagnoses would be taken on clinical grounds, more often than not, with occasional samples being sent to Pirbright to check on the virus, to see that we were dealing with the same strain. The first suspect case would introduce the standstill order (Form C). We wouldn't bring in the infected order until we had laboratory diagnosis from Pirbright, normally about four hours later; there was no great time lapse. That happened in 1981 when I was CVO, and we held fire [confirmation of FMD] until 11 o'clock at night to get the sample investigated at Pirbright.

Hall: Just an addition to that. I am sure the veterinary officer concerned was Cyril Walker, and the diagnosis was taken on clinical grounds alone, nothing was sent to Pirbright.

Taylor: Sherwin is quite right. I do remember a case in Hampshire in 1957 in the New Forest, when there was no FMD in the country. The disease was reported by a veterinary surgeon, and I went along and diagnosed the disease. Four cows were affected. I rang head office and was cross-examined. Eventually I spoke to the Deputy Chief Veterinary Officer and he said, 'Are you quite satisfied it is FMD?' and I said, 'Yes'. He said, 'All right, we will confirm'. There was no material sent to Pirbright until after that particular incident.

The Regional Veterinary Officer arrived towards the evening, and I remember it particularly, because by the time he arrived all the cattle and pigs had been valued

---

[24] See Glossary.

[25] The first FMD outbreak was confirmed in pigs in an abattoir in Essex on 20 February 2001 (FMD/01), the origin for that outbreak, and the index case for the whole epidemic, is considered to have been a pig finishing unit at Burnside Farm, Heddon on the Wall, Northumberland (FMD/04), which was licensed to feed processed waste food under the Animals Byproducts Order 1999. See Auditor General (2002).

and shot.[26] He invited me out to dinner that night to the Crown Hotel in Lyndhurst. That was a thing that Regional Veterinary Officers never did!

Sellers: This is about the initial diagnosis of the 1967 outbreak in the laboratory. I was in charge of the laboratory at the time, because John Brooksby was having a hernia operation and John Davie was doing the actual diagnosis. Although the case came in on the Wednesday night, I don't think we got the sample either until late Thursday or early on the Friday and then we did the usual tests. At that time the usual test was the complement fixation test,[27] which gave an answer in three hours. After that the samples came in, although we didn't have a sample from every outbreak. I think there were something like 250 or 300 samples and they came from outbreaks in new areas, or where the Ministry was doubtful as to what it was.[28]

Source	Samples examined (No.)	Samples from which the FMD virus was isolated (No.)
Confirmed cases	117	114
Doubtful cases	105	19
Total	222	133

Table 2: Isolation of FMD virus O_1 from samples taken during the 1967–68 epidemic.
See Northumberland (1969a), Table 6, 55.

Mr Ken Tyrrell: Coming through in the central requirements was the fact that so many veterinary officers were experienced in FMD and most of us had passed through Pirbright at some stage, where we had been shown what it was, if we hadn't seen it before. Now it actually happened that we in Cheshire had carried out some rather good planning, though we didn't know about it at the time. On 24 October 1967, the day before this outbreak was confirmed in Shropshire, we ran a veterinary meeting in the Rising Sun Inn, Tarporley, where we showed the

[26] Mr Angus Taylor wrote: 'All veterinary officers carried Webley and Scott pistols in their cars at that time. This was stopped in the 1960s.' Note on draft transcript, 19 May 2003.

[27] See Glossary.

[28] Dr Bob Sellers wrote: 'The actual numbers were 355 samples and the results can be found in the Northumberland Report, part 1 [Table 2 above], Northumberland (1969a): 55.' Note on draft transcript, 15 August 2002.

Figure 5: Steer at Pirbright shows excess salivation indicative of the development of FMD lesions in the mouth.

FMD film to local veterinary inspectors. Subsequently, one of those [who attended the meeting on Thursday] rang up on the following Monday and said, 'I think I have something nasty here'. This was in Darnhall, not far from Tarporley. I took Peter McCready with me, who had never seen FMD before, and we confirmed it straight away on one animal. Only one was good enough for me, as I had seen plenty of it in my time. I got it confirmed over the phone, without sending any samples up. Peter McCready stayed on the farm. I came away, and we went off to the big one down in Crewe before we knew where we were. It was quickly diagnosed and quickly confirmed, because, first of all, we were experienced, even though it was a jump of 35 miles from the previous case, or the previous focus in the Oswestry area. Yes, it was in cattle [Figure 5].

Soulsby: Time for one more comment before we move on to the next section. On the sheep that you had, was there ever any despair at this outbreak, as it moved along and got bigger and bigger and bigger?

Rees: I think there was, even in the first week, when it was escalating with no real explanation as to whether they were all secondaries or we had other primaries, and until we investigated the origin, there was obviously a concern about the escalation of the disease. When it got to 81 cases in one day, there were serious thoughts about whether we should blanket vaccinate in the whole infected area.

Morris: I think it is important to recognize that the attitude of the veterinary staff in those days was that speed was essential. We were all schooled that the quicker you killed animals reproducing virus, the better. With Ellis's case the disease was in adult pigs that had been treated for rheumatism for some days, when it was clinical FMD, so there had been a delay. As you know, pigs produce a lot of virus, and the delay gave time for the virus to multiply. The other thing we must recognize is that the whole series of outbreaks was due to multiple primaries, and obviously you will come to that later. The multiple primaries were a result of a known shipload of known infected lamb carcasses but there was no legal authority to seize that shipload or to stop any further distribution. Infected meat was being distributed, and again Howard will know the details better than I on this, but that was what resulted in the multiple primaries.

Soulsby: If we can now move on to policy implementation: how it was organized and implemented and what problems occurred. How did the MAFF veterinarians relate to farmers and to their bosses in London? How did things change during the course of the epidemic? Angus Taylor will address that.

Taylor: I was the DVO in Cheshire when the outbreak occurred. I had a staff of seven veterinary officers, five of whom were very experienced in FMD. Various other divisions or counties throughout the country had similar staff with experience of FMD. That has already been mentioned, I think, by Ken Tyrrell, and is something that is very important to remember.

I have been looking back over the years and I opened the first FMD centre in Cheshire at Crewe in 1967, which was my 17th centre since 1944. We were very fortunate in Cheshire at that time to have had close links with the National Farmers' Union (NFU). We had organized study groups, evening meetings for farmers throughout the county, and we knew all the local secretaries as well as the county secretary. They were a tremendous help throughout the outbreak. We took over the civil defence centre in Crewe on the 31 October with some of the staff from Cheshire and other staff from neighbouring counties. Ken Tyrrell was sent out to the first reported case, Alan Beech of Stocker Lane Farm, Darnhall, near Winsford. He and another veterinary officer dealt with that case. He will probably tell us a bit more about it than I can. Shortly after the first centre in Crewe was opened, one of the veterinary officers in Chester rang me up and said he had another confirmed case just outside Chester. So we set up another centre in Chester itself and finished up with four centres – Crewe, Chester, Northwich and Macclesfield – in Cheshire during the 1967–68 outbreak. I think it is important to emphasize this, because it is quite impossible to control things properly if a centre becomes too large. That may have been one of the features of the present outbreak that some of the centres were much too large.[29]

I should also mention the MAFF set-up for the veterinary staff, for those who are probably not aware of it. At that time we had about eight regional officers and their deputies in England and Wales, and then the DVO who was in charge of a county. Throughout the outbreak the veterinary staff were in charge, in contrast to what happened recently. We very quickly had other cases reported and in Cheshire we were into double figures in the first week. We knew there was something seriously wrong and that it would be a very difficult outbreak. I will always remember one of the deputy chief veterinary officers came down to take charge in the Crewe centre, and we discussed what was developing. The first thing he said after he had listened to me, was that the book of instructions should be thrown out of the window and that we would play this by ear, which is what we did at Crewe. We never referred to the book of instructions after that.

Dr Alan Richardson: I was a veterinary investigation officer at that time. I reported on the first day to Macclesfield. The organization was so structured, and so professionally run, that as a comparative novice, or rather a complete novice, there were no problems coming from the outside. There was always somebody you could rely upon to give you the correct guidance and more or less make sure you didn't go wrong. That again contrasts with the present situation.[30]

Soulsby: I was interested in one of your comments, Angus [Taylor], that some centres were much too large. What was the drawback of the centre being too large?

---

[29] The Northumberland Report described MAFF's regional infrastructure in 1967. See Glossary and Northumberland (1969a): 19–24. Mr Angus Taylor wrote: 'I insisted that the veterinary officer dealing with the report case contact the centre before phoning head office. This enabled us to deal immediately with dangerous contacts or tracings from the infected premises rather than await HO confirmation. In some cases a second opinion might be required before contacting HO and a senior veterinary officer was sent out to the farm.' Note on draft transcript, 19 May 2003.

[30] MAFF's contingency plan for FMD assumed that up to ten premises would be infected, although in 2001 more than 57 premises were infected by the time the first case was diagnosed. No other scenarios were explored, not even one based on the 1967–68 outbreak. An internal departmental review, the Drummond Report of 1999, reported wide variations among the SVS preparations to deal with outbreaks and stated that a rapid spread of FMD would quickly overwhelm their resources. See Public Accounts (2003). See also notes 62 and 116.

Taylor: At Crewe at the peak of the outbreak we had 120 veterinary officers and about 70 technical staff, and that was quite difficult to organize. I understand that in the large centres in the present outbreak they had probably twice that number of veterinary staff, and it would just be impossible to organize them properly. In running an FMD centre, organization is absolutely essential.[31] The difficulty they experienced in the present outbreak was that few of the SVS staff had much experience of FMD.

Meldrum: I worked with Angus [Taylor], my mentor in Crewe, and he's a fine guy to work with because he knew so much about FMD, as did all the local staff. I had come to the centre from Oxford and worked there for 16 weeks. We had a lot of veterinary surgeons, including some from overseas, weren't they, Angus? They came from English-speaking countries for training, and we had temporary veterinary inspectors (TVI) from veterinary practices, and also from the Royal Army Veterinary Corps (RAVC). It worked extremely smoothly. In the morning you would go into the centre from wherever you were staying – bed and breakfast – and would be allocated work for the day. If you were fairly experienced you were given report cases to deal with, going on to farms with suspect disease, and you would work on that farm until such time that it was clarified negative. If it was positive then you would confirm the case with Tolworth headquarters, and get on with valuation and slaughter. It worked extremely well, but there was veterinary control in the centre. It was a centre of reasonable size.

Angus is quite right that we didn't always obey the rule book. For those who know me, I have some experience in using firearms, rifles in particular. For instance, we had the use of a local knackerman in the Crewe centre, who used a high-powered .22 rifle for putting animals down. That was frowned on by Tolworth, but thankfully we carried on using this chap. He was superb and in his hands that rifle was extremely safe and effective. A large number of cattle could be killed when they stood facing you without any movement at all, no rushing round the pens or getting frightened and stressed. It was extremely humane, very accurate, maybe not perfectly safe, but it was safe in his hands. This is one example where we did not follow the rule book and it worked extremely well.

---

[31] Mr Angus Taylor wrote: 'I can recall four centres simultaneously in Somerset in 1958. Senior veterinary officers didn't approve of large centres, but in those days we had about 70 field Divisional Veterinary Officers (now Divisional Veterinary Managers) when in 2001 there were only 23. The Somerset outbreak was relatively small. The Lebrecht management review of 1993–94 was responsible for this cutback.' Note on draft transcript, 19 May 2003. See Lebrecht and Corner (1993) and note 33.

I think there is a very important issue on the size of the centre and that it was under veterinary control [in 1967].[32] I worry greatly about what may be happening at the moment, because at that time – Howard Rees can comment on this later – I have no doubt that we were comparatively well staffed with veterinarians in the SVS. As time has gone by there has been cutback upon cutback, most recently following the Lebrecht Review.[33] It simply means that when a big emergency arose this year, there were insufficient staff available to deal with it, and others had to be brought in, both from other parts of the UK and from overseas.

One other thing, I was talking to Jim Scudamore, the present Chief Veterinary Officer, both at the weekend and also last night, who said that one big difference between what happened in 1967–68 and what is happening now is that now there is no internal administrative structure in MAFF. In those days there was a parallel administration running in each county, a divisional executive officer with his staff, who would deal with the routine administration within the centre. That structure has gone. Jim Scudamore was not able to call upon that parallel support that we had back in 1967–68.

Soulsby: I can confirm that. I was in the USA at the time of the 1967–68 outbreak and I happened to be on the Animals Committee of the National Science Foundation. The Americans sent over quite a number of their veterinarians from the US Department of Agriculture (USDA) and they were highly complimentary as to the way FMD was handled in the UK.[34] They built a lot of their planning for what they should do in the event of an outbreak on the experience that they got over here at that time. I understand they also sent some veterinarians over this time, didn't they? I wonder if they formed the same opinion this time compared with the 1967 outbreak.

---

[32] Mr Keith Meldrum wrote: 'During the 2001 outbreak non-veterinary directors were brought in to manage the control centres.' Note on draft manuscript 17 June 2003.

[33] The 1993–94 Lebrecht management review (Lebrecht and Corner, 1993) looked at MAFF's Animal Health and Veterinary Group, which included the SVS. The Hon. Mr Nicholas Soames for MAFF told the House of Commons in a written answer on 16 February 1994 (*Hansard* 237: Col. 851w) that it was not appropriate to publish its recommendations. Mr Andy Lebrecht was Principal Private Secretary to Mr John Gummer, the Minister of Agriculture, Fisheries and Food, from 1990 to 1993.

[34] The Northumberland Committee visited and took evidence from Denmark, the Federal Republic of Germany, France, The Netherlands, Argentina, Brazil, Uruguay and the USA, including the past and present directors of the Plum Island Animal Disease Laboratory. See Northumberland (1969a): Appendix 1, 110–111.

Meldrum: There was in fact an arrangement set up when Howard Rees was CVO for obtaining staff from six or seven overseas countries on an exchange basis, if there were to be an outbreak of disease. It was Howard and Mick Loxam's initiative.[35]

Rees: Yes, following the experience of the 1967 outbreak we did set up in 1984 an arrangement with CVOs in, I think, six English-speaking countries – the USA, Canada, New Zealand, Australia, Ireland and possibly Denmark – so that in the event of an emergency we could call on them to send us 20 senior staff each. In the present outbreak, I think we had staff from everywhere, including Hungary and Poland, where perhaps they had difficulty in speaking English. We didn't have that difficulty in 1967–68, because all the overseas veterinarians were English-speakers.

Richardson: I worked for four months in Cumbria during the present outbreak with a large number of Americans and I think they have gone home mightily impressed with British farmers, but they have also learned how not to control FMD.

Tyrrell: We were talking about how the Royal Army Veterinary Corps (RAVC) were brought into this.[36] Perhaps just for the record, I can itemize exactly how it happened. Angus asked me to oversee infected places (IPs), disinfection and disposal of animals, and I had the use of quite a few soldiers who were sent down to help us. The problem was that the soldiers had done the disinfection, but nobody [no veterinarian] had the time to go out and certify that they were clean, so I spoke to an army officer called General Staff Officer Grade II (GSOII) up in Blackpool, and he said, 'Well, Mr Tyrrell, what else can I do for you?' I said I could do with some NCOs from the RAVC to go round and see that the farms have been properly disinfected. They came down, but very quickly the RAVC said, 'Well, we can't send down NCOs without officers'. Suddenly eight veterinary officers from the RAVC arrived, and two or three were allocated to Crewe, some went to Chester. The RVO in Chester rang me up and said, 'What's this, general mobilization, Ken?' That's how they arrived on the scene.

Soulsby: In the commentary about this part of the outbreak, there was the question of how the government vets, the MAFF vets, related to farmers, and what the relationship was between farmers and stock owners, and the vets and their superiors in London? Was there a good rapport between the divisional office and the farmers, and the stock owners and the local vets and others at that time?

---

[35] Mr Howard Rees wrote: 'Mick Loxam was Director of Field Services from 1984 until 1987.' Note on draft transcript, 2 June 2003.

[36] See Auditor General (2002): 17, 26–27.

Figure 6: Mr Angus Taylor receives an inscribed silver salver from the Cheshire Agricultural Society in March 1968. L to R: Lt Col. Sir Richard Verdin, Mr Angus Taylor and Miss Mary Brancker.

Taylor: Yes, there was excellent cooperation. We knew all the local secretaries of the National Farmers' Union (NFU). The county secretary had his office in Crewe and at the height of the outbreak he was in my office every day and if we had any difficulties with farmers, the NFU representative sorted it out. Relations were not always cordial, it's only natural in an outbreak of that description when farmers are very worried and upset. I think the most difficult thing of all is when you are slaughtering contiguous stock [from adjacent premises], which are healthy. I usually undertook this if I could, as it was difficult to persuade a farmer that we should slaughter healthy animals, but we only did it when there was a connection between his animals and the infected farm, or perhaps because it was next door to the infected farm. But on the whole, relations were extremely good and I think Mary Brancker will remember an occasion at a meeting in Crewe where the Cheshire Agriculture Society presented a silver salver to me on behalf of all the veterinary surgeons who took part, which I still have. I don't think any silver salvers will be dished out for the present outbreak.

Rees: My impression was there was no great opposition from the farmers, but Sherwin [Hall] mentioned the Oswestry market. When the decision was made to disperse the animals, there was local opposition at that stage. I think you mentioned that one of the MPs was going to raise a question in Parliament.[37] But as the market was all dispersed by 28 October, and nothing happened afterwards, that opposition disappeared, but there was initial opposition to this dispersal of the market.

---

[37] See page 16.

Figure 7: Preparing a pyre for slaughtered cattle and sheep.

The other point I think we should mention at this stage (my colleagues will correct me on this) was, as far as I was aware, that all animals on infected farms on contiguous premises were buried or burnt on the premises during this outbreak. I don't remember ever moving any animals from an infected farm. The only occasion that I can remember this being done was during an outbreak in Aberdeen in the early 1960s when the disease broke out in the market in the middle of Aberdeen, and there was no way of disposing of them in the town. The animals were transported immediately outside the town on to council grounds and buried. That's the only occasion I remember in the past of animals being moved off an infected farm.

Hall: Just a very quick example of a farmer who was not very cooperative. He wouldn't allow any veterinary officers on to the premises, so a stop was put on his milk. He couldn't send his milk to the creamery, so when his bulk tank overflowed he suddenly became compliant.

Soulsby: I wonder whether there were any appeals at that time against the action that was being taken, as indeed there are now.

The Duke of Montrose: I was just wondering if you actually had to carry out any contiguous culls without being able to convince the owner that it was necessary.

Rees: Well, I think there's a different terminology used now.[38] I don't think in those cases we slaughtered out many contiguous farms. We slaughtered dangerous contacts that might be part of a farm. It wasn't always easy, as Angus has mentioned, to convince the farmer with healthy stock that they should be taken [slaughtered], but they were taken on the basis that they might have been infected, but were not infective at that stage. So to cut the scale of the operation down, dangerous contacts were taken, but then buried on that farm. They weren't taken miles away by road. I don't know, Angus, if that happened in other places, but that's what happened in Oswestry.

Brent: I assume that farmers were compensated for animals that were culled, is that correct? Were they given their full market value? I think I heard a 'yes' from the audience.[39]

Meldrum: Just one point about burying on the farm. That is absolutely right, but later on, Howard will remember this, we became increasingly concerned after 1967–68 that there were a number of pig farms with no land on which you could bury or burn, and on an individual county and farm basis the DVOs were encouraged, required in fact, to make contingency plans for the disposal of livestock from those farms, should there be an outbreak of notifiable disease there. Subsequently, by the way, in SVD in the early 1970s, we frequently took pigs away from the infected premises for processing up at the de Mulder rendering plant at Nuneaton in Warwickshire, but this was SVD and not FMD.

Dr Walter Plowright: This is a small query. Were there any restrictions on veterinarians going from farm to farm at that time? I think that arose later, because people were shown to have nasal carriage of virus for some time afterwards. Secondly, to what extent were strict precautions taken in moving from farm to farm, the sort of thing for example that applied to the staff in Pirbright?

Tyrrell: Might I just clarify terminology? In 1967–68 we talked about slaughtering out dangerous contacts, but we did not, repeat not, slaughter out contiguous contacts. 'Contiguous' is a word that is used in 2001. We slaughtered out dangerous contacts, because they were on the other side of the hedge, or where there had been some means of contact.

Soulsby: Any comments about Walter Plowright's question about restriction on movement of individuals?

---

[38] See Glossary for contiguous and dangerous contacts.

[39] For details on compensation, see Northumberland (1969b): 59–66 and 130.

Figure 8. Cattle attendants decontaminating their protective clothing by spraying with alkaline disinfectant prior to leaving one of the animal isolation units at Pirbright, *c.* 1967.

Mowat: A small piece of information. Experiments were in fact carried out with staff at Pirbright. Members of staff were invited to stand in loose boxes where infected animals were held. Air samples were taken to establish the level of virus that was being excreted by the infected animals. I think the longest period in which nasal carriage operated was about 48 hours or so, and this was done by taking nasal swabs from the people who were exposed.[40] Beyond that, I think, the natural cilliary activity in the retro-pharyngeal area dispersed the virus.

Morris: Could I support that and say that every veterinary officer in the country in 1967–68 had a steel box in which his FMD kit was kept and it was to be used for nothing else. That protective clothing consisted of a heavy rubber coat, boots with smooth soles that could be easily cleaned, a sou'wester and leggings, and it was kept exclusively for FMD work, just as we had pistols that were supplied so that we could dispatch the diseased animals at once without any delay. One washed off [the kit] before going on [to infected premises] and before coming off at every stage. When I say wash off, I mean literally wash off, so that any dust or anything that might be carrying the virus was washed off that clothing. When

[40] Dr Bob Sellers wrote: 'The FMD virus was recovered from the nose of one person at 28 hours after exposure, but not at 48 hours. In nine other cases no virus was recovered at 24 hours after exposure. See Sellers *et al.* (1970).' Note on draft transcript, 15 August 2002.

the pressure was on us, when I was on report cases and would have to leave a positive case and then have to go back, I would have had all my clothing disinfected.[41] You usually had a chance to send your suit to the dry cleaners and you would have a bath or a shower or whatever. You would be back in action the next day, because you had to be, the pressure was so great. When the pressure eased off the veterinary officer would not go back immediately to another case. I was not aware myself of any disease arising from us going to one report case to another.

Sellers: If you look in part 1 of the Northumberland Report, it gives the number of outbreaks that were spread by veterinary surgeons or by people [Table 3].

Attributed to	Number of outbreaks
Animals	1
Vehicles	18[a]
Veterinary surgeons	6
Other persons	4
Milk products	9[b]
Hay	1
Recrudescent outbreaks	12
Total	51

(a) 15 milk lorries (8 milk tankers, 7 churn collections), 2 stock lorries 1 slurry tank; (b) 8 skim milk, 1 churn washings.

Table 3: Sources of infection in FMD outbreaks during 1967–68.
See Northumberland (1969a), Table 5, 54.

Noel Mowat has mentioned the nasal work and we didn't do this until after the 1967–68 epidemic. I myself don't think the nose is important, far more important is the other experiment we did when we got virus off samples from clothes. My view would be that the danger is more of a vet or anyone else going from contact with one animal to contact with another animal, without any disinfection in between.

[41] Mr James Morris wrote: 'Lysol has been shown to be a poor disinfectant for FMD virus. I preferred to use a detergent Teepol, which we used for fowl pest work, because of its cleansing effect.' Note on draft transcript, 23 May 2003.

Rees: Taking up Walter's point there were no particular restrictions on private veterinary surgeons being on farms. Obviously they were instructed to disinfect properly when going on and coming off, [Figure 8] but there was no stopping them going on for emergency purposes. Maybe Mary will join in on this. The question of infections through the nose wasn't something of concern in field operations at that time. I don't know how dangerous it would be. I can't remember how many times you had to blow your nose at Pirbright after coming through the showers, but certainly it wasn't an issue at that time in the 1967 outbreak.

Soulsby: I didn't get an answer to my question whether there was any appeal against action that was supposed to be taken at that time, compared with now.

Rees: Farmers could object, but we could carry on and slaughter. If they disagreed with the valuation of the official valuer, they were allowed a certain amount of time – a matter of hours – to bring on their own valuer, but they didn't need to sign the valuation form. We could carry on with the slaughter, and they could appeal later if they wished. It would go to arbitration, but there was no delay. It was left for a couple of hours if they objected to the valuation, but they didn't have to sign this form necessarily and we carried on with the slaughter.

Meldrum: I am sure you are thinking about something else, and that's to do with the Animal Health Bill.[42] This Bill, as I read it, Lawson [Lord Soulsby], would give the Ministry far wider powers than they have at the present time to slaughter contiguous stock over a very wide area, while as a number of people have said in the cases we are discussing in 1967, the cattle or stock on the farm were either on infected premises, the owner's other premises, or there had been a close contact, and in the view of the veterinary officer, the other stock had been exposed to the virus or may have been exposed and they should be taken out [slaughtered] as a precaution. But they were not normally some miles or kilometres away unless they were on the owner's other premises.

Soulsby: Well, we are just about coming to the end of that bit of the programme. Are there any other points before we move on?

Taylor: Just one thing occurs to me about disinfection. In Cheshire we employed the local fire brigade, who went on to farms and disinfected vehicles and strengthened their straw pads at the end of the road. They were very useful. In fact, the most recent Chief Fire Officer in Cambridgeshire often reminds me that he was at Crewe during the 1967 FMD outbreak. It was a very satisfactory method of getting preliminary disinfection done.

---

[42] The Animal Health Act received the Royal Assent on 7 November 2002.

I will just mention one other thing. We don't want to give the impression that everything was perfect in 1967–68, it certainly wasn't. We soon ran out of contractors, particularly during the third and fourth weeks of the disease. We had over 50 outbreaks in Cheshire on the day 81 cases were reported in the whole country. We were certainly getting a bit behind with the slaughter and the disposal of animals, but nothing like what's been happening recently. Eventually we called in national contractors, Wimpeys, who I think were used in Shropshire as well as in Cheshire and that decision certainly increased the efficiency of the job we were doing.

Soulsby: The message that seems to be coming over to me, apart from the odd shortage of facilities like transport, is that there was good collaboration between vets, farmers, the army, police and the fire brigade. Is that a fair conclusion?

Tyrrell: May I just correct what Angus said about the national contractors. Wimpeys were used in Cheshire, but in Crewe we initially used a contractor who was an engineer from the Mersey and Weaver water authority and it was Mike Doody who subsequently was given an MBE for his work there. He was a man of vision. His diggers (used for excavating streams and rivers) were lying idle because of FMD, and he offered them to me. With some hesitation I took them on, and he took over the whole business from there on. Because he was a man of vision he had parks in Middlewich filled with contractors' plant that could move off within half an hour, and he had diggers, bulldozers, sprayers, all [types of] equipment. His was a wonderful expertise that was subsequently recognized by the Queen [Figure 9].

Rees: May I just add to that, Chairman. One of the problems was that most animals were buried and when you have 81 outbreaks in one day and 80 the next day and another 80 the following day, there was difficulty in keeping track of where the diggers were. One DVO at the time, George Taylor (unfortunately he's dead now), had the initiative to hire a helicopter to locate the diggers, and for his efforts he was given a real telling off by head office for the cost of the helicopter.

Dr Maurice Allen: I was in the research service and joined in the Cheshire investigations. I am the third admirer of Angus Taylor's set-up in Crewe. I think the conclusion that we perhaps haven't identified clearly is that the whole success was due to the education and up-to-date experience of all the veterinary staff involved. Having been involved myself in this current outbreak I think there's an abysmal shortage of education and up-to-date experience [of the sort] that existed in 1967.

Figure 9: JCB backhoe loader, an example of the machinery used to prepare burial sites in 1967.

Taylor: Howard mentioned the helicopter. I eventually got the bill for it from headquarters and they said, 'Can you please account for all these journeys made during the outbreak?' I can't remember what the sum was. I simply wrote, 'I am sorry I have no record of this, you have probably sent it to the wrong Taylor.'

Meldrum: The helicopters were also used for carrying chains. Why? One thing we ran out of in Cheshire was chains to pick the cattle up on the diggers and drop them into the holes. Chains were in great demand and the helicopters were used for transporting them from farm to farm. It was a very effective and fast method of movement.

Hall: I have a note here that the helicopter cost £75 per day and you had to guarantee three hours flying at £27 an hour.[43] Mike Doody, the chap from the Mersey and Weaver River Board, was in charge of the plant, which was the

[43] See 'FMD 1967–68: Historiography source sheets. Typescript by Sherwin Hall, 1968. Full set nos 1–245 and part set nos 1–101', held as AC.41 by the Library of the Royal College of Veterinary Surgeons, London.

largest plant hire operation in the country at that time. The kind of thing that happened was that the officer in charge of an IP would see a low-loader coming along the lane with a digger and he would say, 'In here, in here', and of course it wasn't meant to be there at all. But he waylaid the plant in order to get his job done. The people back at base didn't know where the equipment was and the only way to find out was to have a helicopter to see what was going on.

Tyrrell: George Taylor had his helicopter and Doody wanted one. I spoke to my GSOII in Blackpool and said I wanted a helicopter and he said, 'Why not, Mr Tyrrell'. But Tolworth sat on us so Doody said, 'Well, that's no good', and he went off and hired his own. It was wonderful – I had 11 trips in it!

Morris: If I may, I think I am correct in saying that I was the first one to use a helicopter or helicopters in that outbreak. That was because, and it's a very important point, we were desperate. We would not move infected animals, dead animals, or livestock, off an IP or put healthy places at risk from the movement of livestock. Quite early on I had an infected premises on a hilltop, and although there weren't a large number of animals, a mixed collection of sheep and cattle, the only way we could get things to it was through another farmyard. The lane came up through another farm. We couldn't bury on this hill, so it was decided to burn, and the only way we could get the material there was using an RAF helicopter, or two RAF helicopters, I think. They took it in turns flying up a supply of sleepers and coal, and all the necessary things to the top of the hill for me. We had a fire right on top of the hill. But that was very early on and I don't think these other chaps had really got on to choppers by then.

Professor Alan Glynn: How many viruses were carried on these helicopters?

Morris: They did not touch down, they hovered and dropped the stuff from a big net underneath. As long as you weren't standing underneath it, all went well. They actually did not land, but were able to release the nets, go away and return with another full net.

Soulsby: Can we now move on to the next topic, that is the farmers' and the veterinarians' response. Mary Brancker is going to deal with vets in practice and the contrast in the response of farmers who were slaughtered out, and the farmers under restricted movement.

Brancker: There was very good organization in those days, practically all veterinary surgeons after they had been qualified six months were made local veterinary inspector (LVI), or whatever you called them in those days. We of course thought that the whole-time people [SVS] were pretty idle and useless, and they were quite sure that we were of no value at all, but we all knew each other. Once there was a common cause then we could all work together, because we knew each other's weaknesses and strengths. I would like to endorse what Angus said that it made a tremendous difference to have a team like that.

I am going to look at the farming community and the veterinary profession from the social point of view. We have heard a lot of technical stuff about machinery and so forth, but I think we need to look at what the outbreak did to the social life of the farming community. It was a very rough time for both groups, the veterinary and the farming, but they had a disagreeable time for different reasons. The farming people, whether they were in the infected area or anywhere in the country, lived with fear. If they were actually in the infected area, the fear was worse, but it was all over the whole country. No one knew for certain whether they were going to get the disease. Now that is a pretty unpleasant way of living, if you think of it. Then they had the loss of income, varying in amount, but there was a certain degree of loss, I think, on every farm. They also had no social life and, if you are feeling pretty low, you can't even have a night out. So we have got to look at the farming people from that point of view, and realize that considering how we usually regard them – they complain like mad and are always miserable – but in this case they rose to the occasion, and, though they were miserable, no more so than usual – or at least they didn't appear to be.

The veterinary people, the whole-time people as we have heard, were well trained, experienced and went into superb action. The veterinary people had this crowd of farming people who they had regarded as useless, and discovered that when the farmers put their minds to it they weren't too bad. From the point of view of the veterinary volunteers, they were away from home in fairly uncomfortable situations, and usually working long hours. One thing that we have got to remember is that there were no mobile phones in those days and if you wanted to talk to the wife or to a partner, you had to queue for a public call box, and if you took too long over a call, the people in the queue behind them got irritated. So that is a small thing, but I think it should go on record, because it was from a social point of view, quite important. I would ask you also to look at the wives who were left behind to cope with life for weeks on end, because once anyone got into the infected area, well, that was it. If you asked, 'Where's so and so? Oh, he's in an infected area, oh, I see, yes. Well, when he comes out, tell us.' It was almost as though he had gone to the North Pole. And the veterinarians were also doing a job that was not theirs by nature or by training really. Diagnosing disease and therefore death was a very depressing way of living. Can you picture what it was like living on a farm in an infected area, a ghost farm, because it had no animals? I think that needs to go on record and needs thinking about.[44]

I have spoken about those at what you might call 'the coal face', but higher up there was good cooperation as well. There was Henry Plumb as Vice-President of the NFU and I was President of the BVA and we have been fast friends ever since. That, I think, tells you something about the relationship that developed among a lot of other people as a result of the epidemic in the 1960s.

Soulsby: Thank you, Mary. May I just ask the first question. Was there any concern on the part of the vets who volunteered at the large-scale culling that was taking place? Was there any feeling that this was not the right way to go?

Brancker: No, I think if there had been they went to see the DVO, had a discussion on it, and were satisfied. I don't think there was any problem like that. One thing if I can just add it on, was that, of course, in the practices, if they were entirely agricultural, there was probably only one veterinarian left. Their livelihood had gone, because there was no routine work, and the one person who was left had to do 24-hour emergency service for weeks on end. It was pretty miserable there. Both the farmers and the vets, to my mind, did a good job in those days.

Richardson: Could we say a bit about the culling? I think there were particular criteria in 1967; animals that were killed were diseased animals or were reasonably expected to become diseased within a short period. There was a very different feeling about it, compared to killing at the behest of a computer model that took no account of local circumstances.

Lord Plumb: I think what Mary has said presents the picture that existed in those days and even more so now. One of the problems I think we face now – it may be out of order if I talk about the present outbreak – is that there are no men on the farms. In those days at least there was a gang and if they had to stay on the farm, then at least they were all together and could share their thoughts, and talk together about the problems. Now there is no one to talk to. Another major difference now, which Mary quite rightly referred to, is the camaraderie we farmers used to have with each other and the veterinarians. In my own area for instance, living in Warwickshire, the two large [veterinary] practices, as far as large animals are concerned, have both gone and there are no [veterinary] people on the ground. This, I think, is one of the major differences we are facing today as opposed to then. We had those [supportive] relationships, it was quite excellent.

---

[44] For images of the 1967 outbreak, see Whitlock (1968): 59; Hughes and Jones (1969): 64.

Soulsby: Mary has mentioned the loss of social life. I have some stepbrothers who lost a lot of sheep in a contiguous slaughter in 2001. They hadn't been off the farm for weeks and they were beginning to get a bit itchy. One of my brothers said, 'I would give anything just to go along to the pub for a pint', but they couldn't leave the farm. There are an enormous number of things that don't seem to come out, except possibly in a session like this. They never get on to the news or in the newspapers. Any other comments?

Meldrum: When I was in Cheshire I thought the farmers were absolutely fantastic, the way they responded, in the way they cooperated with us, and I cannot recollect any problems at all in that respect. But I wonder whether Angus or Howard would take the view that we seem to have gone downhill since that time. I certainly have a very distinct feeling that farmers nowadays are less willing to comply with the disease control regulations that are laid down for their benefit. Certainly that has been my experience through BSE and I think it is still the situation now. In those days [1967–68] I had a feeling both during the FMD outbreak and elsewhere that farmers were trying to comply with the laws, not in every detail – their records may not be fully up to date – but in general terms. I don't think we had the problems that we have at the present time, where farmers seem to go out of their way to try to evade controls that are laid down for their benefit.

Brancker: I was thinking that I haven't been controversial enough. Perhaps I should have said something that you would all contradict.

Soulsby: May I ask the Duke of Montrose about such issues in Scotland. Any comments about the Scottish situation, farmers and collaboration?

Montrose: Certainly, the control measures were more readily accepted in Scotland this time round. We certainly had memories of the 1967 outbreak in Scotland and that slaughter and compliance was required. My view on the comments that Keith Meldrum made about farmers' attitudes is that I would only say that it is possibly an outcome of the mass of regulations that are now included on almost anything that you try to do. Farmers have gradually adopted the idea that they can't do them all [the regulations], and they are going to skip some of them. You begin to have so much less respect for the regulations that are offered.

Soulsby: Well, we are doing well. If there are no further comments about that part of the programme, we can turn to the media's response and someone who's quite happy with media and media participation is Keith Meldrum.

Meldrum: A very odd introduction, my Lord Chairman, but I will take that up with you later privately. OK, I have had my fair share of media exposure in the last few years, but going back to 1967–68, as a veterinary officer working entirely on farms, I was not exposed to the media at all. They didn't impinge in any way on the work I was doing. The press were not intrusive in the way that they have become in more recent times. Indeed I can't recollect seeing photographers at the [farm] gate with long-range lenses, trying to get pictures at all. As far as a veterinary officer was concerned on the farms, and I dealt with a fair number of farms in Cheshire, I guess we had no problem. I don't know whether Angus was doing his normal job and protecting us from the outside forces, be they Tolworth or ministers or be it the media, but I think everything has moved on apace since that time.

I looked specifically at the Northumberland Report and the section of that report entitled 'Information Services', and it's quite clear that they were looking specifically at providing information to the media, and in particular to the BBC, to advise farmers in particular. There's one lovely piece in here, in one particular paragraph, where the Northumberland Committee concluded that they agreed with the recommendation put to them that an appropriate time to have bulletins available to the press would be at half-past six in the morning and between six o'clock and half-past six in the evening, indicating that the press were somewhat more malleable than they are at present. But, as I say, things have moved on apace. During the early 1970s, when we were dealing with SVD (later on I will talk I hope about the waste food controls), I don't recollect any particular problems with the press at that time. I do, however, remember very clearly that there were problems with the press later on in 1981. The amount of press attention for the single case [of FMD] in 1981 on the Isle of Wight seemed unbelievable. I had just moved to Tolworth – my last round of working in Tolworth – I remember thinking: 'Golly, if we ever had a major problem, the press would be here all the time on our doorstep, not only that but they would be on the doorstep of farmers and everywhere else, trying to get their own stories'. Maybe I can put this into perspective. I know that Alec Brown, Howard Rees's predecessor [as CVO from 1973 to 1980], told me on one occasion that he had only one agriculture correspondent, Mr Peter Bell, that he [as CVO] ever spoke to. While I, on the other hand, had a different experience. I seem to recollect that at the turn of last year when the BSE report was coming out, I had in excess of 50 approaches from television, radio and the media in general for interviews and to comment. That is the sort of activity that you now get involved with, they soon find your name, your phone number and they will make approaches.

Putting the Northumberland Report into context, if you look at Lord Phillips's *Report on the BSE Inquiry*,[45] there is neither substantive comment nor recommendation made about government relations with the media. Yet that is absolutely critical. I can understand why the Northumberland Committee commented the way they did on information services.[46] In that context I guess you can understand why the spin doctors are now on top of the pile, very important people so far as government and ministers are concerned; they make sure that what information is provided to the media, the press and so forth, is used sensibly. One of the major problems I think anybody who is working in government now faces is how to inform the public, the consumer, in a neutral way, without the information being spun out of all existence by others, particularly by tabloid papers that make their own headlines, and have no real interest in the facts. I have felt that since I retired four-and-a-half years ago, because I wanted to keep up to speed, to know a little more about BSE.

It's very difficult indeed to get the facts. You are always told, 'Go and look at the website'.[47] OK, websites weren't in existence in 1967–68 and they are now. How many times in a week would one be advised to go and look at a website? You could spend all your time looking at websites and I don't find them all that easy to find, then identify and extract the information that I want, and I certainly don't want to spend all my time on my computer. Things have moved on tremendously since 1967–68. I would be interested in the views of Angus especially, and Ken and Howard, on whether or not they saw the situation at the time differently to me. Then it was very easy by comparison with what it is now.

Sellers: I was at Pirbright in the 1967–68 epidemic, because we were then, as now, separate from the Ministry of Agriculture. All the press would get at us, to

---

[45] Phillips (2000).

[46] Northumberland supported the use of communications, particularly when locating an FMD control centre. At that time full services included telex, car and pocket radio telephones, walkie-talkie sets and radio links with observers in helicopters. Other recommendations included trained public relations officers, informative films and leaflets and large durable signs. Northumberland (1969b): 66–71. See also Anon. (n.d.b). for comparison with 2001. For internal working party's discussion on information and advice, see TNA(PRO) MAF 287/494.

[47] Websites sometimes change locations, but more often a link remains, although the original page has been removed. In March 2002, the Wellcome Trust and the Joint Information Systems Committee (JISC) undertook a feasibility study into web archiving, including the legal implications of copyright, data protection, and defamation. The reports were accepted in December 2002. For further details, see library.wellcome.ac.uk/projects/archiving.shtml (visited 29 May 2003).

try to get round the backs of the Ministry, and you had to watch how you dealt with them. One thing I noticed, and I would agree with Keith Meldrum, was that the agricultural correspondents were very helpful. One used to live four doors along from me in Guildford, and I was able to discuss what was going on with him. He made a very good point, which was that he used to write his bit for the paper and then the subeditor used to come along and shorten and alter it so as to put a different slant on it. And it was important how one was reported in the papers – you had to learn what to say. There had been criticism in the press from the medical profession about the disinfectants being used in the field and I was testing disinfectants. I said that a certain disinfectant was less effective, and later on I read in a paper that the disinfectant was not effective! That was the difficulty. The same happened again in the 1972 swine vesicular disease (SVD) epidemic. When I saw work on disinfectants reported in the House of Commons – I read what was there – it was completely wrong. It made me wonder whether you can believe anything that goes on in the House of Commons or even in the House of Lords.[48]

Soulsby: I have some queries here: did the media understand the problem? did they get in the way? I think you have partially answered that question, [Keith]. Agricultural correspondents did understand the problem I presume, but the more general press might not have done so.[49]

Sellers: I'll just add another point. I thought they set up a separate parallel dummy operations room at Tolworth to deal with the press. This was, I think, during the swine vesicular disease outbreak, so the press could come along and watch what went on, because of all the trouble the Ministry had at Tolworth in the 1967 outbreak.

Unidentified member of the audience: An amusing little anecdote from 1967 shows that the press could also be difficult then. One of my colleagues wouldn't allow a newspaper reporter on to an IP. Shortly afterwards he had to eject a drunken workman from the premises. This man was photographed and appeared in the local press with the caption: 'Ministry Vet leaving property'.

---

[48] Dr Bob Sellers wrote: 'The references for disinfectants are as follows: Sellers (1968); Herniman *et al.* (1973). The reports in the agricultural press and in *Hansard* were made in 1967–68 on disinfectants for FMD. There were criticisms in the SVD epidemic in 1972–73 as the disinfectants recommended for FMD were not always suitable for SVD.' E-mail to Mrs Lois Reynolds, 3 June 2003.

[49] There was only one press office centre for the whole of the West Midlands. See Hughes and Jones (1969): 69–70. Hughes and Jones felt that the *Cheshire Chronicle* kept the public informed of the spread of the disease, including names of farmers, which MAFF did not. See Northumberland (1969b): 69 and note 46.

Rees: On the question of the difference in the media coverage for 1967–68 and at present, it was certainly my impression that the media acted very responsibly in 1967–68. We didn't have the problem that they had recently where the press tried to sensationalize everything. They did show photographs of burial pits and burning etc., but in general they were fairly responsible in their reporting. I noticed a big difference in the 1981 outbreak, as Keith has mentioned, where we only had one case on the Isle of Wight. As soon as it was confirmed and we were burying animals the next day, the press had a helicopter over the farm taking pictures. We didn't want this, because all they wanted to do was sensationalize this burial. We had the Ministry of Defence declare it an exclusion zone, so they couldn't fly over the farm. Even with one case, we had to have morning meetings with the press and television to explain the circumstances. There was a big change from 1967–68, even to 1981, in terms of the media involvement in outbreaks.

I went up to Oswestry about two or three weeks after the 1967–68 outbreak started. I had been given the task of investigating the origin, because up to that point there had been no time to investigate the origin, as staff were fully occupied in dealing with [new] outbreaks. When I arrived the RVO told me that some press people wanted to come in that afternoon to discuss the origin of the case, and would I talk to them? I said, 'Well, I have only just arrived and haven't started the investigation yet'. He said that it didn't matter, 'Just go and tell them what you are going to do'. I had to explain all the possibilities we were going to explore, and they were quite satisfied with that. We had no antagonism from the press in those days.

Dr Tony Garland: My Lord Chairman, I am here as an imposter. During the time of the 1967 outbreak I had been seconded from Pirbright to the regional laboratory for FMD in East Africa. We did have some problems of our own with FMD there. I have been back at Pirbright during the nine months of this present outbreak. I would like to make some comments on the media, who have been extraordinarily intrusive at Pirbright, taking up an inordinate amount of senior staff time. Of course there is the dilemma of wanting to give people factual and correct authoritative information on the one hand, but also to spend time on the important scientific work at a time when there are far too few people at Pirbright to cope with a crisis of this type.

On another aspect of information, we are often asked to comment on parliamentary questions at Pirbright and it is just as well that we are, because some of the information in the draft answer would have been a masterpiece of misinformation had not somebody who knew something about it had a chance to comment. Finally, concerning the websites that Keith mentioned, I think that the MAFF/DEFRA website that was in action during this recent epidemic has been an exceptional example of a website giving authoritative information, quite exceptional. But I remember manning the hotline one day and a farmer's wife was asking for information on disinfectants and I said, 'Well, if you go to the MAFF website you will find an enormous amount of helpful information there'. She said, 'So, what is a website?' I think that's quite typical. It is wrong to assume that everybody has access to modern information technology.

Soulsby: I think you make a very important point, because not necessarily apropos of the 1967 outbreak, but in animal disease and in agricultural information in general, many officials just assume that everybody has a computer, that everybody is computer literate. One day I mentioned in the House of Lords that marginal farmers, for example, may not be able to afford a computer and, if so, they can't get the information that other people would normally obtain. I think that's an important point. Any other points?

Mowat: Thank you, Chairman. I can't resist the temptation to tell you a short and, I think, amusing anecdote about some things that have already been mentioned – disinfectants, air transport and the Isle of Wight. In the 1981 outbreak we used to get letters from various people offering amateurish advice. As you know already the FMD virus is extremely sensitive; if you change its environment, make it acid or alkaline, the capsid[50] of the virus falls apart and it becomes noninfective. We had a letter on one occasion from a chap who said, 'I am a chemist and I understand that the virus of FMD is very susceptible to pH changes. It seems to me that the answer to your problem is very simple with the Isle of Wight. All you have to do is hire a small fleet of light aircraft and spray the whole of the island with weak vinegar, the virus will fall apart, end of problem.'

Soulsby: Can we just conclude this section on the media's response, that indeed the press didn't get in the way and, if I am not misinterpreting what Keith said, that they did help rather than hinder the MAFF effort. They did understand the problem 30 years ago. Indeed, they helped much more than they hindered.

Hall: Another quick one on that. The press and information services was one of the topics that I was specifically examining, and almost without exception they did say that on the whole the press were very good, as was the BBC. The Towcester centre had some problems, and they recorded the fact that a cameraman from Anglia TV forced his way on to the premises and had to be evicted, but not before being

---

[50] See Glossary, page 95. See also Figure 10, page 42.

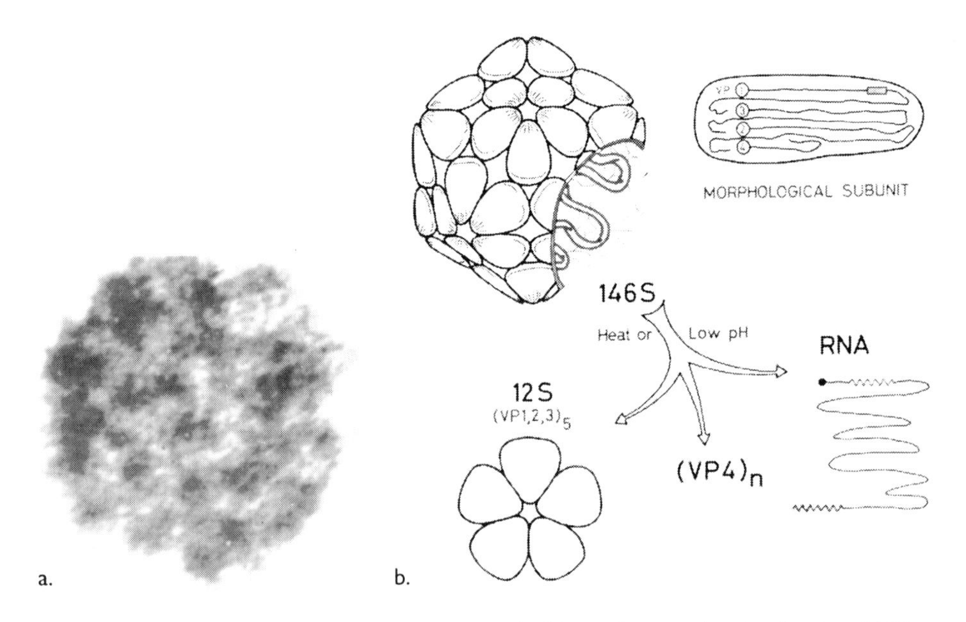

Figure 10: 'The components of an intact virus particle (a) are illustrated in the drawing (b). The particle consists of 60 copies of four proteins and a single molecule of RNA (ribonucleic acid) 8000 bases in length – the infectious component. The RNA is the blueprint for replication and is located within the capsid or empty outer shell which therefore protects the infectious element of the particle. The capsid is constructed from subunits (12s) – the latter value being the sedimentation coefficient of the subunits in a sucrose gradient. Each subunit is made from four polypeptides (VP1 – VP4). The intact particle is approximately 27 mu in diameter, has a sedimentation coefficient of 146s and is very similar in size to particles of poliovirus.' Dr Noel Mowat, 6 August 2003.

thoroughly soused in disinfectant. They also had a freelance television cameraman with a telescopic lens, so press intrusion was beginning, even in those days.

Meldrum: Coming back, if I may, Chairman, to the Northumberland Report. Quite clearly the report saw information dissemination at two levels. One was at headquarters level. They commented that there was a difficulty because Whitehall was obviously many miles away from the SVS headquarters in Tolworth, Surrey. I think, Howard, when we had the outbreak on the Isle of Wight in 1981 a press officer, Tony Colmer, was seconded to Tolworth. Of course, that didn't arise at the present time, because Tolworth is no more; all the Animal Health and Veterinary Group are now in Page Street, London.[51] Northumberland also recommended in the report that there should be a local

[51] See note 17.

network of information officers, which was done subsequently, and ran for many years. I don't think that network did any national briefing, but they were extremely valuable for local television, local radio, and local dissemination of information, because farmers need to know what is going on. I have heard that recently. Farmers need to know what is going on, have details of outbreaks, details of infected areas, and I think there is a major issue here that was picked up post-1967–68 and dealt with, I think, adequately, if not very well. That has now fallen apart and is an issue that has to be addressed at the present time. May I just ask Angus to comment on his experience in Crewe, because he would have picked up the press if they were hammering on his door, so to speak.

Taylor: Funnily enough I don't remember a lot about that, except I had an agricultural correspondent from the *Cheshire Chronicle*, who frequently came to see me. He was extremely good. He never altered what I told him, and that was very unusual for a reporter. One other thing, a lot of the presswork was dealt with by the RVO at Oswestry, because I remember reading complaints from the local papers that when they tried to get through to Oswestry it was very difficult, and therefore it would have been much better if we had dealt with it locally. I don't remember any problems.

Soulsby: I must say I always feel that if you can keep the local press informed, you have them on your side; they can do an awful lot of good in the local area, compared with the national press that are out for a different sort of story with dramatic headlines.

Mr Gareth Davies: I was just reflecting. I was in East Africa at the same time as Tony Garland, and as he said we had some problems out there. He omits to mention that in his vaccine trials in Embakasi, Kenya, he lost one vaccine trial because the control cattle were eaten by lions that had got underneath the fence from Nairobi National Park.[52]

Tyrrell: Might I make one comment that hasn't been covered in our discussion so far this afternoon? That concerns the action of the local authority and the police during 1967–68, particularly licensing for welfare movement and licensing within [the restricted area] from farm to farm. The police played a very valuable part in this exercise and they really did a splendid job. The farmers came into a central point, explained what they wanted, looked at the maps, and were given a licence, either supervised or unsupervised, depending on the necessity.

---

[52] Dr Tony Garland wrote: 'The incident of the lions from Nairobi Game Park was reported by the BBC.' Note on draft transcript, 8 May 2003.

There was none of this 'three-weeks' notice', sending letters off to Leeds, looking for a licence, as they have done in 2001.

Taylor: Ken Tyrrell has raised a very important point. I do remember that we had a police officer in the office at the Crewe centre full time, and he issued all the licences for welfare and abattoir movements following a veterinary inspection.

I would like to make one other point. I think when we declared infected areas, we always tried to have an abattoir within the infected area, so that farmers outside the five-mile area but within the infected area could send animals for slaughter. This doesn't seem to happen nowadays. Of course we haven't nearly the number of slaughterhouses now that we had in 1967–68 and that probably accounts for it.[53]

Soulsby: Well, if there are no further comments, we now go on with our last four sections, three major points, and then a general discussion afterwards. The first one is vaccination and Pirbright, and Noel Mowat is going to lead the discussion.

Mowat: Thank you, Chairman. I would like to take this opportunity to do a little flag waving, if I may, on behalf of Pirbright, the place I used to work. It seems to me that the first question that might be asked about Pirbright and vaccination is, 'Why should a country in which FMD is not constantly present, that's not endemic (enzootic), invest much money and time and effort in supporting a sophisticated high-security laboratory and also in research on vaccines and vaccination procedures?' The answer, which I think is rather far-seeing, is that this is done to gain reflected benefit. Over 50 years ago it was thought that if the Institute for Animal Health at Pirbright could develop improved or new vaccines and control methods, and promote their use in the countries from which the UK obtains its supplies of meat and meat products, the reduced incidence of disease in those countries should result in a much lower likelihood of importing the virus and subsequently the occurrence of outbreaks in this country. In general I think this has proved to be the case. In comparison with the sporadic episodes of FMD in earlier years,[54] it's worth noting the absence of outbreaks from 1968 until the small episode in the Isle of Wight in

---

[53] There were 860 abattoirs in England in 1984, and 316 in 2000. Answer to Parliamentary Questions, *Hansard*, 8 March 2001, **364**, col. 345W. Mr Angus Taylor wrote: 'EU abattoir regulations caused the closure of many small efficient abattoirs because the owners couldn't afford to carry out the alterations demanded. Hence the necessity to carry cattle long distances for slaughter, thus increasing the risk of spread of disease if an FMD outbreak occurred.' Note on draft transcript, 19 May 2003. See also note 15.

[54] See Figure 12 on page 47.

1981, and the gap between that outbreak and the recent one starting in February 2001. Now I am not taking the credit on behalf of vaccination entirely, clearly there were changes in the policies about the type of meat products that could be imported, and that was significant, but I think that vaccination has made a major contribution in reducing the weight of infection in these countries.

It's widely accepted that the Institute has long been at the forefront of developments in the understanding of the epidemiology and the pathogenesis of the disease and also in major improvements in vaccines and this has resulted in the Animal Virus Research Institute, as Pirbright was called at that time, being officially appointed by the Food and Agriculture Organization of the United Nations (FAO) as the World Reference Laboratory for FMD.[55] It was thought in the 1950s and 1960s that with many parts of the world constantly affected by FMD, what was needed was a cheap and effective vaccine, and by analogy with yellow fever and smallpox, the answer to the FMD situation was a live attenuated vaccine.[56] After about ten years of blood, sweat and tears, involving much lab work and field trials in various countries, it was clear that the inherent high rate of mutation in the FMD virus genome was an insurmountable obstacle in the development of reliably safe (I emphasize that word 'safe') and highly immunogenic vaccines. However, results in Holland with the Frenkel-inactivated vaccine,[57] prepared from healthy cattle tongue tissues obtained from abattoirs, showed that successful vaccines could be made. However the extent of production was limited by the amount of tissue available. The emphasis on vaccine development at Pirbright changed then from live attenuated strains to inactivated preparations, following our fortuitous finding that a continuous cell line called BHK21[58] was highly productive of virus and this in turn led to the development of technology and methods necessary for the large-scale industrial production [Figure 11] and manufacture of vaccines, and made possible the very large amounts of vaccine needed for national mass vaccination campaigns. Another important development at Pirbright was the demonstration that totally

[55] See note 8.

[56] Brooksby (1967).

[57] See also Brown (2003); Frenkel (1947).

[58] Dr Noel Mowat wrote: 'There were also limitations on the total amount of vaccine that could be produced. These problems have been overcome by the introduction of virus production in a continuous cell line (baby hamster kidney, BHK21) [Mowat and Chapman (1962); Capstick *et al.* (1962)] and by the use of one of the aziridine compounds, such as acetylethyleneimine [Brown and Crick (1959)].' E-mail from Dr Noel Mowat, 29 April 2003. For further details, see Mowat *et al.* (1978).

Figure 11: Industrial-scale equipment for the manufacture of FMD vaccine, *c.* 1966.

safe vaccines could be made by the use of one of the aziridine compounds such as acetylethylenimine, known as AEI, or BEI, substituting that for formaldehyde, the inactivation agent which was traditionally used in the preparation of many killed vaccines. At that time[59] some of the outbreaks in continental Europe were clearly attributable to the use in the field of vaccines in which there were still small amounts of infective virus. The studies at Pirbright on virus inactivation and the production of safe vaccines made a significant contribution to the reduction in the numbers of outbreaks and the eventual control of the disease in Europe.

With the availability of large amounts of safe vaccine, national mass vaccination campaigns became possible. The need for this becomes obvious when one looks at the numbers of outbreaks occurring in some European countries at this time. In Figure 12 you will see that in France in 1952 there were some 320 000 'foyers' and the translation from French is foci or nucleus, that is, small outbreaks. Also in Holland, and Germany, the disease was frequently, if not constantly, present. It was only after the introduction of mass vaccination which you will see indicated by the letter 'V' (see Figure 12) that the situation improved significantly. The policy of national vaccination was then espoused and promoted

[59] Beck and Strohmaier (1987).

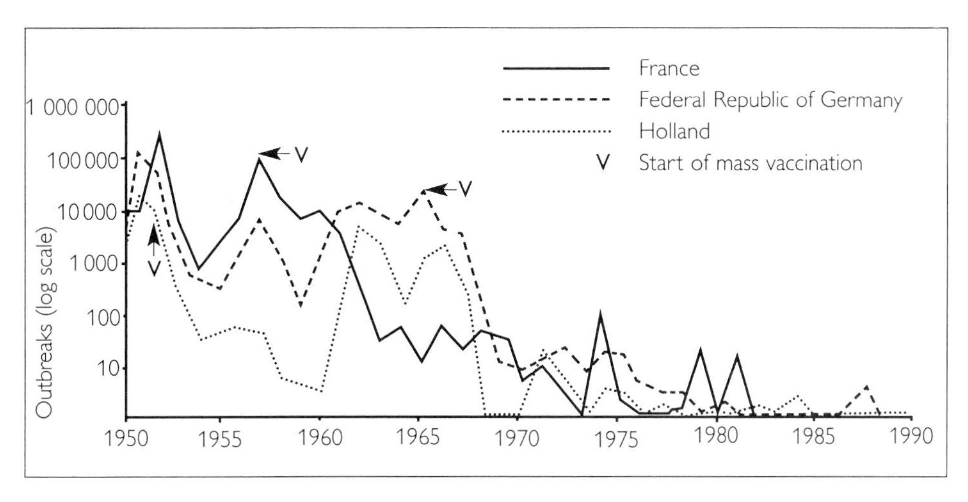

Figure 12: The results of mass vaccination campaigns on the annual incidence of FMD in three European countries, 1950–1990, provided for the seminar by Dr Noel Mowat.

by the European Commission. The object of these national campaigns was to reduce the weight of infection to the point where a policy of zoo-sanitary measures, such as slaughter, movement controls, disinfection, etc., and, where necessary, ring vaccination,[60] could be introduced.

It will be obvious that the costs of these campaigns in terms of materials, time and labour were very large, but they continued to the point at which the total number of outbreaks in Europe annually were either nil or in single figures, and cost–benefit analyses of the policies by the Commission in Brussels[61] clearly indicated that a change to zoo-sanitary measures was warranted. Consequently in 1989 compulsory vaccination in the countries of the Common Market was no longer required by the European Commission.[62] During the same period, from the mid-1960s onwards, some of the major international [pharmaceutical] companies, who I won't mention, who had been producing FMD vaccines in the meat-exporting countries of South America, started production using the new technologies and since then control of the disease has been much improved as can be seen in southern Brazil, northern Argentina and Uruguay – the so-called

[60] See Glossary.

[61] For further details of EC cost–benefit analyses, see European Commission (1989) and Glossary.

[62] EC Council Decision No. 90/423/EC of 24 June1990 fixed the deadline of 1 January 1992 for FMD vaccination in EU countries to cease. For background details of vaccination in the EC, see Glossary. See also Donaldson and Doel (1992); Leforban (1999); Leforban and Gerbier (2002).

tripartite area. In conclusion, I feel it has to be said that the work of the Pirbright Institute in the development of a safe, modern, industrially produced vaccine, has contributed significantly and made possible the ultimate success of the control policies based upon the use of vaccine.

Sellers: I would like to add to what Noel has said. One of the reasons why the live attenuated vaccine failed was that it caused lesions and the virus in the vaccine used in Israel at the time, was completely different from the A_{22} virus that was sweeping the Middle East.[63] One of the main developments[64] since has been the choice of a strain for the vaccine by its relation to the strain circulating in the field and this is a very important point. I myself am quite old, and I get my flu jab every year, and they tell me that they put in the strains that are most current at the time in the vaccine. We have been doing the same at Pirbright since about 1967, so we have been prepared for the outbreaks that were likely to occur.

Mowat: May I support what Bob has been saying. Perhaps I should have emphasized that with a live attenuated vaccine, the time, and the amount of effort necessary to achieve a virus strain which is attenuated and usable, is virtually unpredictable, whereas with inactivated preparations, provided you have a method for producing lots of new infective viral antigen, the time is much more predictable and is much shorter than that which would have to be devoted to the development of new live vaccines.

Plumb: Chairman, naturally I would like to come in on this, if I may when we deal with the Northumberland Committee Report. I think vaccination was the biggest issue and certainly we spent more hours talking about this subject in that committee of inquiry than we did on anything else. I seem to remember at the time that we were concerned that there were some 77 different varieties or strains of the virus. If that is so, how can we prepare for a strain such as we apparently have at the moment compared with that which came from South America? Secondly, the argument recently has been on the question, if the animal is vaccinated, whether it has to be destroyed? And, does the product [the meat] from that animal also have to be destroyed? It seems to me that there's quite a

---

[63] Dr Bob Sellers wrote: 'A_{22} was a new subtype that differed from A_5 subtype used at that time in inactivated and live vaccines. A_{22} first appeared in Iran in 1964 and was found later in that year throughout the Middle East and in the Soviet Union republics north of Iran.' Note on draft transcript, 22 May 2003. See also Northumberland (1969a): 'The nature of the disease', Memorandum submitted by MAFF, Appendix 2, 112–114.

[64] See page 70 on A_{15} Thailand.

muddle as far as people are concerned in today's terms on the possibility of both long- and short-term use.

Davies: May I come back to the European situation? I was involved in the cost-benefit analysis that led to the nonvaccination policy and the decisions taken in the late 1980s.[65] The true situation in Europe over the 1980s is not widely known. From 1968 onwards, I believe there were only two outbreaks of FMD in the European Union (EU) which came from outside. The big breakthrough was that we stopped importing meat on the bone, and the two outbreaks in Denmark were both due to an accident at the Insel Riems FMD Laboratory near Greifswald, in what was East Germany. Apart from that, all the outbreaks were home grown, and by that I mean that they were all leaks from vaccine laboratories, or as in the case of Italy, they were due to the production and distribution of vaccine from government laboratories which contained live virus. The big effect of the nonvaccination policy was to shut down a lot of these plants, to reduce the sources of live virus in Europe; and that policy paid dividends up until now, when we have had viruses bought in from another part of the world.

Mr Chris Schermbrucker: I want to give an answer to Lord Plumb's first question about how to cope with 77 threatening strains of virus coming from all round the world, with increased air travel and people travelling around the place, and the sort of difficulties of the kinds of undesirable meats coming into the airports of this country these days. From the vaccination point of view, the 77 problem was resolved a long time ago at Pirbright. It's an unfortunate fact of life that one of the characteristics of FMD is that it produces these variant strains. One of the main jobs of the vaccine producer is to keep on top of the field situation in that respect, and the UK is in a prime position, in having the World Reference Laboratory for FMD based at Pirbright in the government part of the Institute, so that the monitoring is going on all the time. The other fortunate fact of life is that among the strains of FMD one finds the strains that protect really very well. Of course we also find a lot of other strains that don't protect so well. The vaccine-producer's job is to find the ones that do protect well, with good vaccinal properties. Here is a good example to give you, the recent Pan-Asian Type O that unfortunately arrived in this country [in 2001].[66] By the time it had arrived here it was very well characterized and there were very effective vaccines available for it.

---

[65] See Glossary for description of EU cost–benefit analyses.

[66] Knowles *et al.* (2001, 2002).

I would like to just add a little bit to what Dr Mowat said about the vaccines. I can assure him and others here that the development work on the vaccines goes on apace and that the vaccines available at Pirbright are completely safe, and they are appropriate, in that the strains for the vaccines are prescribed nowadays, and they will do the job, as they have done in the other countries of Western Europe, which acquired the same status as the British Isles, as Dr Mowat said, from 1991 onwards. Many countries in South America have also recently brought the disease under control and eradicated it. There has been recrudescence in South America and those countries have had to go back to vaccination again.[67]

Rees: I think we are very fortunate in the UK in having Pirbright at our disposal, giving us the expertise that we need on occasions like this. So much so that we are the envy of all the other countries in Europe who have tried desperately to get us to close it down.[68] And Chris will remember the battles we had with other countries in maintaining Pirbright as an FMD reference laboratory. They argued that we were dealing with exotic viruses and this was a danger to the whole of Europe. We managed to overcome this and Pirbright continues.

Looking at the inactivation of vaccines, the 1981 case with us was due to the use of improperly inactivated vaccine in France, where they were vaccinating pigs[69] in Britanny with improperly inactivated virus in the vaccine. This was the origin

---

[67] Mr Chris Schermbrucker wrote: 'Chile, Uruguay, Paraguay, Argentina and three southern states of Brazil – Rio Grande do Sul, Santa Catarina and Parana – all managed first to control and then eradicate FMD using vaccination programmes with good zoo-sanitary measures. They all achieved recognition by the OIE as "Free of FMD without vaccination". Unfortunately a few years later there was recrudescence of the disease in Uruguay, Paraguay and Argentina, and they had to reintroduce vaccination. The disease was eradicated once again, but Argentina has declared that they will continue the vaccination for four years in the first instance and will then reassess the situation.' Note on draft transcript, 29 May 2003.

[68] Another review of Pirbright was conducted in July 2002, which concluded that given the 'continuing danger of known and novel exotic diseases of large farm animals entering the UK, increasing international travel, population (and livestock) movements, removal of international borders to trade, climate change and threats of agricultural bio-terrorism lead us to the view that the UK has an absolute requirement for [such] an Institute' (page 24). The Committee members were: Professor Keith Gull, Dr Richard Cawthorne, Dr Nick Coulson, Professor Tony Minson, Professor Tony Nash, Professor John Preston, and Dr Paul Burrows for the Biotechnology and Biological Sciences Research Council as Secretary. For the report, see www.bbsrc.ac.uk/news/reports/pirbright17_7_02.pdf (visited 26 June 2003).

[69] Dr Bob Sellers wrote: 'Pigs were not vaccinated prophylactically in France in 1981. The vaccine was given to cattle in the area at the same time as *Brucella* vaccine. FMD virus in the improperly inactivated vaccine infected cattle and spread by some means to pigs.' Note on draft transcript, 15 August 2002.

of the 1981 outbreak. All I can say is that we are tremendously fortunate in having this expertise at our fingertips here.

Meldrum: Can I just pick up a comment from Gareth [Davies]. I am not sure whether I heard him correctly. He was talking about outbreaks of FMD in Europe between 1978 and 1988. I have some notes here, because and I think between 1978 and 1988 there were 31 primary cases of FMD in the EC. Of these, eight were from sources outside the EC and of the 23 that were home bred inside the EC, in 13 of those 23 cases there was an association with vaccination, either leakage from a laboratory or failure to inactivate vaccine. While talking about Pirbright, I would like to put something else on the record, and I totally support all the comments made about the eminence of Pirbright and that we are very fortunate to have a laboratory of its excellence in the UK. Yes, there were in fact many people who suggested that Pirbright should be closed and that we in the UK should use reference laboratories outside the UK; luckily sense prevailed and money was found to upgrade Pirbright.[70] But to put this in context, Pirbright did have problems in earlier days. I remember in 1970 that there was a leakage of virus outside the high security area[71] into some cattle, it didn't matter very much and nothing really happened. The cattle outside the high security area went down with FMD and VOs in the south-east region were rushed into Surrey under Eric Hendrie's command. We were chasing our tails around Surrey, round Pirbright, for a few days, but of course, there was no spread. But what's more important, is that thereafter, I believe, Pirbright upgraded its security arrangements[72] to have double high efficiency particle abstractions (HEPA) filtration and there has

---

[70] Mr Keith Meldrum wrote: 'The Pirbright laboratory was subject to a series of fundamental reviews in the 1980s. A large capital investment programme took place at that time and ran for ten years or so.' Note on draft transcript, 17 June 2003. The amalgamation of Compton and Pirbright in 1986 into the Institute for Animal Disease Research was part of the Agriculture and Food Research Council (AFRC) strategy to reduce expenditure on institutes in order to increase funding to universities. See Professor John Bourne's statement of evidence (no. 107) to the BSE inquiry, available at www.bseinquiry.gov.uk/files/ws/s107.pdf (visited 8 April 2003). See also Anon. (nd.c).

[71] Dr Bob Sellers wrote: 'There were two incidents in 1970. The first involved a package from Tunisia containing an FMD sample that had leaked in the local post office and the farms on the postman's rounds had to be checked. There was no disease. In the second, virus spread from an isolation unit to a holding unit at Pirbright and the cattle developed FMD. Precautions were taken within a radius of two miles around the Institute, but no case of the disease was found. See MAFF (1970).' Note on draft transcript, 15 August 2002.

[72] Dr Bob Sellers wrote: 'The extra filtration had been introduced in 1960 after transmission of FMD from Pirbright to a local farm.' Note on draft transcript, 15 August 2002.

never been any suggestion of any problem or any leakage of virus from that laboratory since that time [1970]. The same standards are now being applied to other laboratories in the UK that are handling particularly virulent viruses.

Sellers: One of the leakages from the laboratory occurred in 1967, just before the big outbreak, and we learnt a lot from that, especially on the pathogenesis and spread of FMD. We had pigs in one isolation unit and sheep and cattle in another unit nearby, that wasn't under filtration. What happened was that we had been supplied with duff filters, so air containing virus was blown out by the extraction fans straight across into the unit with the sheep. We didn't find any disease until the cattle went down. Now if Pirbright can miss a disease in sheep, if there was disease in sheep in this instance, I have every sympathy with the vets in this present outbreak who are trying to look for lesions in sheep. When we analysed what had happened, we found no disease in the sheep. There were some that had nothing – no virus, no antibody – although they had been there for several days; some had virus in their throat; some had virus in their throat and antibody; and some had antibody alone. So a virus escape can be of help as well as a problem, provided the conditions of escape are analysed.

Davies: Can I come back to the discrepancy between Keith's figures and mine? I said there were two outbreaks that I believed originated from outside Europe and he has eight. When we got the heads of the various FMD laboratories around the table in Brussels, and put the data to them, some of them [laboratories] resolutely refused to concede that in fact the outbreaks they had in their countries were due to their own vaccine laboratories, notably the French. We weren't going to die in the ditch over this, we knew we had won the case in any case, so I think when the figures came out, we allowed them. They couldn't tell us where the outbreaks had come from, but we put it down that they had come from outside.

Plowright: Could I just ask our friends from Pirbright what the time interval was from resistance to contact challenge after inoculation of the vaccines available in 1967? And, what was the duration of immunity thought to be? In what species were they effective? While others are thinking about the answers, I will tell you about another interesting outbreak illustrating the dangers of introduction of FMD virus in research materials. In the 1970s we were looking to produce an antibody, a serum, against classical swine fever, and using pigs in gnotobiotic isolators. We imported an attenuated swine fever virus from a French institute and put it into these pigs and they developed FMD very quickly.[73]

---

[73] Dr Walter Plowright wrote: 'This outbreak was never publicized but confirmed.' Note on draft transcript, 18 May 2003.

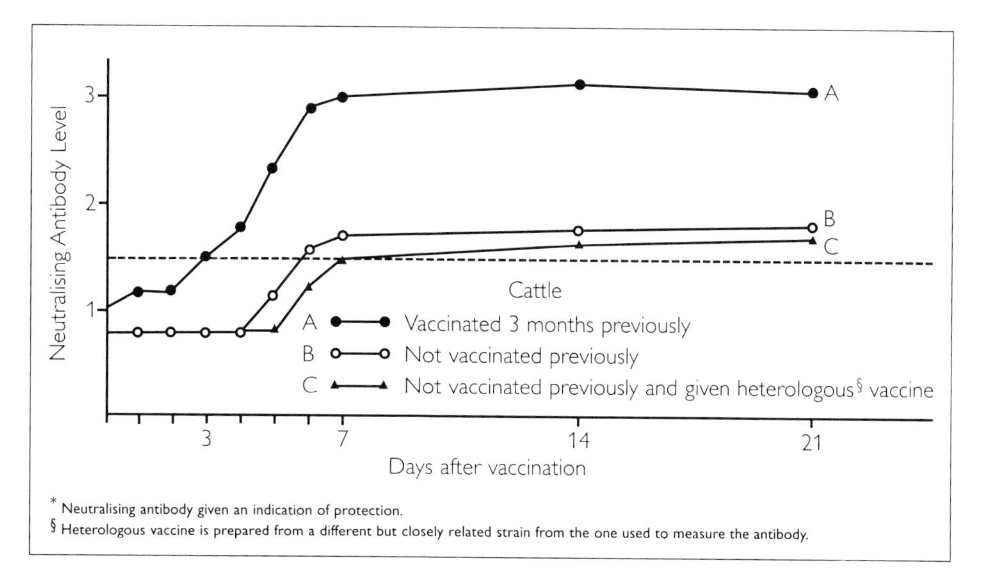

Figure 13. Neutralising antibody response of cattle to inactivated FMD vaccine. Antibody level is given as Log_{10} of the geometric mean titres of a number of sera. The broken line indicates the level at which protection may be expected. See Northumberland (1969a), Figure 4, 66.

Mowat: I am not sure that I can remember all the details, but certainly at that time the era of concentrated purified vaccine had not arrived and I seem to remember that the conventional wisdom was that one had to wait something like seven to ten days for demonstrable protection to be available.[74] You got a broad type of immunity, IgM antibody being formed, and then subsequently the specific IgG which was much more related to the antigenic identity of the vaccine. I think at the time it was regarded that in cattle you would have to wait something like ten days for a useful protection and it would reach its maximum at about 21 days, and it would wane subsequently and you would have to revaccinate again in six months in order to push the level of immunity up for continuing protection.

Dr Hugh Platt: As regards the use of vaccine for control of an outbreak situation, how much of a risk is the carriage of virus in vaccinated animals going to be?

---

[74] Dr Bob Sellers wrote: 'In the Northumberland Report, Part 1 [Figure 13 above] the antibody response to FMD vaccine in cattle is given. This shows a level of protection six days after primary vaccination with the vaccines available in 1967–68. In another experiment at that time vaccines given four days before challenge with FMD virus gave protection.' Note on draft transcript, 15 August 2002.

Sellers: When we did experiments exposing cattle to infected pigs, we found that there were three stages. The first stage was when people came into contact with infected pigs, the virus got on your clothes, and so cattle got virus on their hide and skin. In the second stage virus that had been taken in through the nose to the throat, multiplied there and virus was exhaled in the breath. The third stage was after 28 days – when the carrier had virus present in the throat. I don't think there has been any proven case of a vaccine carrier passing it on to another animal, either from a recovered animal or a vaccinated animal.[75] The only thing people do worry about is, if the animal has the virus in its throat and it goes to the abattoir, whether there will be virus around that area that might get passed on.[76]

Woods: Going back to 1967, I would like to know where the impetus to vaccinate came from? Who was in favour of vaccinating? Which sort of vaccinating was discussed, and who set the time-scale for vaccination and made all the plans for vaccination?

Rees: It certainly wasn't me. As I mentioned earlier, while the disease was escalating in 1967 there were fears that it was getting out of hand, and the possibility of vaccination came up as a means of controlling the disease and stabilizing the outbreak.[77] I don't know if Mary was involved at this end, but as I mentioned a group met in Oswestry control centre on the 2 December to devise a plan for vaccination and they went into all the pros and cons of how many veterinary surgeons would be available. I think they did highlight how many were available to carry out the vaccination, and it would have to be completed within ten days and vaccine was purchased at that time. The disease incidence then peaked and started coming down, so vaccination was abandoned, but the initiative came from the Tolworth end. They wanted to consider the pros and cons of vaccination, the consequences, if they had to carry it out at that stage.[78]

Sellers: I don't remember who made the decision and so on, but I remember at the time Noel said to me, 'We are living in history, the Ministry are going to vaccinate'.

Mowat: In answer to your question I think it's worth emphasizing that in the first half of the last century there was a culture that couldn't think beyond the fact that the principal method of controlling this highly transmissible infectious

---

[75] Thomson (1996).

[76] See Anon. (n.d.a): 13.

[77] See notes 16 and 20.

[78] See Northumberland (1969a): 72, and note 20.

and contagious disease was to stamp it out, to slaughter animals. I don't think people ever thought that they would deviate from this, because in all the episodes in the first half of the twentieth century every outbreak was eventually controlled and the disease never became enzootic in this country. Each episode was controlled by the slaughter method, so this was the accepted, successful method of dealing with the disease, and consequently vaccination was very much at that stage a fall-back position, in case this became a disaster not previously experienced. I think it was a cultural thing in many ways.

Tyrrell: It's perhaps worth recording that after 1967–68 all Ministry veterinary staff had instructions on how to arrange vaccination programmes, as regards recruiting staff, hiring cold storage, distribution centres, etc., so the plans were all there ready to be used if the eventuality arose. I think they must have got lost in the meantime![79]

Soulsby: Keith says they are still there, but obviously they haven't been dusted down. I suppose Fred Brown's work on subunit vaccine started sometime after the 1967 outbreak. [To the audience] When did he start looking at the subunits and trying to make a vaccine out of that?[80]

Rowlands: We started doing that work in 1981.[81]

Soulsby: Some time after the 1967 outbreak.

Rowlands: There is one point I would like to make. We have heard from Noel that there have been enormous strides in vaccine development, pioneered at Pirbright, but I wonder to what extent this has fallen off. Obviously the incentive to work on vaccine tends to disappear if vaccination is stopped in Europe. We have heard a lot about some of the disadvantages of current vaccine technology, the delay between vaccine and induction immunity, and perhaps even more important the lack of current vaccines in developing good secretory immunity. I think there is a number of ways in which we can envisage better vaccines yet and I would hope that this year's experiences will prod the funding of further developments of vaccines for this disease and perhaps even encourage the contemplation of the possibility of global eradication in the future.

---

[79] Mr Ken Tyrrell wrote: 'Which is a polite way of saying NFU and EU opposition to vaccination.' Note on draft transcript, 20 May 2003.

[80] See Brown (1999, 2003).

[81] Bittle *et al.* (1982). See also Boothroyd *et al.* (1981); Brooksby (1981a, b).

Soulsby: Some people in the audience will remember the cost–benefit evaluation of Power and Harris,[82] where they conclude that slaughter policy is more acceptable economically and more realistic than vaccination. Any comments on that?

Rees: I think it came out of the Gowers Committee Report as well, they looked at this and said that the preferred policy for Britain would be a stamping-out policy without vaccination. That was their sound view. On this question of carrier animals, may I just read a quote here from the delegation that went to renegotiate the 1928 Bledisloe Agreement[83] in Argentina. Sir Gregor Henderson was one of the three people there and I presume this quote is from Gregor:

> If, however, a vaccinated animal has been exposed to infection at an earlier date, it may have become a carrier with persistence of virus in the tissues of the pharyngeal region. The fact that virus may be present at this site in apparently healthy cattle is beyond doubt, and the possibility of contamination of the carcass, and in particular the tongue, from this site cannot be dismissed.[84]

Whether this contradicts what was found later I don't know, but this was Gregor Henderson's view in 1968.

Soulsby: Difficult to confirm.

Sellers: I think that if the virus remains in the pharyngeal area, as I said, it may be there at slaughter. Certainly no one has shown for certain in the live animal that

---

[82] Power and Harris (1973) conclude that 'on the basis of purely quantifiable factors, and on the assumptions used, a traditional slaughter policy would be less costly for the community than a vaccination policy. But it needs to be emphasised that there are many non-measurable factors that ought to be considered in arriving at a final assessment, in particular the cost to farmers of greater uncertainty and stress under the slaughter policy.' Quote on page 594.

[83] The agreement imposes measures to reduce transmission of FMD virus from the South American countries of Argentina, Brazil, Uruguay and Chile, where FMD is endemic, by stopping the import of the virus in fresh meat or meat products. A report from A G Beynon, W D Macrae and W M Henderson following a veterinary visit to these countries in April 1968 recommended that the agreement be revised in light of improved knowledge and, in particular, to restrict bovine imports to fresh boneless meat and to introduce a ban on tongues and offal. See a summary of the Bledisloe Agreement of 1928 in Northumberland (1969a): 70, and Appendix 6, 128.

[84] Anon. (n.d.b): quote on page 13.

it comes out and infects other animals, and that's in the field or in the laboratory.[85]

Schermbrucker: Continuing the theme of the so-called carriers, there's no doubt that following the discovery by Dr J G van Bekkum in Holland in 1959,[86] cattle that have recovered from natural infection with FMD may have recoverable live virus in the oro-pharynx. That applies whether the cattle have been vaccinated or not. Tony Garland, Gareth and myself were in Kenya, at an interesting time when the vaccine lab was owned by the Wellcome [Foundation] based within the headquarters in Pirbright. A very successful vaccination campaign was initiated there,[87] compulsory vaccination, not for the whole country, because our limited resources started in the high-production, high-rainfall central areas, and was expanded outwards as the resources became available. British scientists working there with the Overseas Development Administration (ODA) carried out an interesting survey where they assessed the rate of carrier animals in the vaccinated cattle in the programmes and the rate of carrier animals in the unvaccinated naturally infected cattle in the nonscheme areas. From that one piece of work there was an indication of a much lower rate of carriers in the vaccinated cattle than in the unvaccinated cattle. My own view, having worked with several overseas governments in control programmes for FMD, I think there's a human psychological problem at work here, that because there's live virus obtainable, people are worried to death about it. As several of my colleagues have already said, we don't know of a good case where a national programme has been damaged in any way by recrudescence of this carrier virus. I discussed this subject at some length with Professor Gordon Scott in Edinburgh and Gordon said, 'Where there's no disease, in a strictly epizootiological sense, where there's no disease, there's no actual carrier'. The word 'carrier' in FMD should be used in inverted commas. His definition of this kind of animal who will have virus there for only a limited period of time afterwards, he calls it the 'inter-epizootic host' of the virus.

Garland: Just one or two comments which really don't relate too closely to history. I would like to endorse what has been said that there isn't much in the way of hard evidence to show that the carrier animal poses a risk of transmission of disease to other susceptible animals. There is some evidence from the field.

---

[85] See Thomson (1996).

[86] van Bekkum *et al.* (1959).

[87] Mr Chris Schermbrucker wrote: 'See the Government of Kenya Veterinary Department annual reports for 1968–79. See also Berger *et al.* (1975).' Note on draft transcript, 29 May 2003.

I know of two in Europe and several in southern Africa, but they are anecdotal. Whenever people have tried in the laboratory to transmit from a known carrier to a known susceptible [animal], those experiments have been unsuccessful and various types of stress have been applied. I remember when we were first shown the carrier state by van Bekkum[88] and probably didn't believe it very much at Pirbright, he asked if we've had some recovered animals, 'I will show you', and he did. We then thought, 'Ahh, this explains everything' and we better just do some confirmatory work. Lo and behold we couldn't transfer it, and other people have found the same. My comment, however, and this is not a point that's very often made, is that these experiments necessarily involved extremely small numbers of animals and my own view is that the work that we have done proves pretty well that if transmission ever occurs, it's a very rare event, but not that it can't happen. The significance of this, if it does happen, of course, is very, very serious. So I don't think we can dismiss it. That's my personal opinion.

Plumb: Gentlemen, we are all searching our memories. Just for the record, work on vaccination was going on in the USA between 1967 and 1969, whether it was under Fred Brown[89] or his predecessor. I remember the Duke of Northumberland and Bill Weipers going there, because, in particular, I remember complaining because the whole research station is on Plum Island, so therefore I thought I had a right to go with them. Nevertheless, I do remember them coming back with quite a favourable report of what was being said.

Rees: To put the statement in the Bledisloe Report in context, what they were looking at was the danger of importing tongues from Argentina, with the possibility that there could be virus in the tongues. The issue was whether the tissue would be dangerous, not so much from animal to animal, but if we imported raw tongues.

Davies: I think the big difference between the 1967 epidemic and this present epidemic is that the 1967 epidemic was a matter for the government, the profession and the industry. I think in the present epidemic, the public have a considerable interest, because of the vast amounts of money that have been spent, and also because slaughter is up there in front of you on the TV. I have been working with DEFRA recently on what might be called 'political trigger

---

[88] Dr Bob Sellers wrote: 'It was Paul Sutmoller who came to Pirbright to demonstrate carriers.' Note on draft transcript, 15 August 2002.

[89] Dr Bob Sellers wrote: 'Dr Jerry Callis was Director of Plum Island Animal Disease Laboratory in 1967–69. Fred Brown did not arrive there until the 1980s.' Note on draft transcript, 15 August 2002. Dr Callis gave evidence to the Northumberland Committee.

points' at which they [DEFRA] might trigger vaccination. One would be when the resources for culling are overwhelmed; the second one is that the public simply won't have it. I think that's the big difference between now and then, and that if this happens again the public will turn round and say, 'We are not going to have this'. I remember when the committees in Brussels approved the nonvaccination policy in Europe in 1988,[90] a Frenchman turned to me and said 'Wait until you have two or three outbreaks, the public won't wear it'. Well, they have worn it actually, but I don't think they intend doing so forever.

Soulsby: Any further comments on vaccination? We have run a little over time on that issue. I wonder if we can now turn to the meat question and Howard Rees is going to introduce that.

Rees: I was despatched to Oswestry, probably two or three weeks into the outbreak in 1967 and was told to investigate the origin of the infection. My first task was to look at what we called the FM1, the report of the actual outbreak. On that form there is a paragraph asking for the name of the farmer's butcher. The name of the butcher was given, and someone from the centre had then rung up this butcher and asked, 'Where do you get your meat from?', 'What imported meat do you handle?' And he replied, 'Only New Zealand lamb'. That was written down on the form and was the end of the original origin inquiry. Having been involved in inquiring into origins in the past, I never believe what I am told the first time round, particularly by butchers. I didn't go to see the butcher, but I did visit the farm and discussed it at length with Mr Ellis. As usual, people are so upset in those first days that they can't recall everything that happened. But looking at all the immediate outbreaks following, it was obvious that the Ellis case was a primary. The disease in other cases was not as old as the Ellis case, so it was quite clear that this was a primary, and not a secondary from any undisclosed infection. We looked at the possible links with the two other outbreaks that had occurred in Hampshire and Warwick earlier in the year and there was no connection at all. There was no connection with the 1966 Northumberland case, where Pirbright said there was an antigenic difference in the strain of the O_1, so there was no connection there.[91] We established no connection at all with previous outbreaks, and were satisfied this was a new outbreak and that there was an origin somewhere. I enlisted the help of the meat division at Tolworth, who traced imports into this country from Argentina. We

---

[90] See note 62.

[91] O_1 is a subtype of the FMD virus, first described by Vallée and Carre (1922).

had a veterinary attaché in Argentina, and we knew they were having problems with FMD at that time and it was an O_1. They identified a consignment of 770 sheep carcasses that had come into Tilbury [docks, London] in late August 1967, which had been dispatched to the Fatstock Marketing Corporation (FMC) in Wrexham. At that time there was a dock strike as well in Southampton, so there was a disruption in the supply of New Zealand lamb, which resulted in a disproportionate amount of Argentine lamb going up into the countryside, when in the past normally most of the Argentine lamb was distributed to urban areas. This was an exception, and this consignment had gone to an FMC depot in Wrexham. I still didn't go near the butcher.

I went up to Wrexham, and went through all the invoices of this consignment, as to where it had been dispatched to, and there was a name of a butcher in Oswestry, but it didn't tie up with the name of the butcher that was involved with Ellis. Luckily some of the workers at the depot knew that this particular butcher was having financial problems at the time, and didn't trade in his own name, but used the name of one of his employees. So all the invoices were made out in the names of his employees. So then I had details of 107 carcasses that he had received out of this 770. Armed with this information I then went to see the butcher and again asked him what meat he handled and he again told me only New Zealand lamb. I asked 'Are you sure of that?' He said, 'Yes, only New Zealand lamb'. So I then showed him the invoices for 107 carcasses he had received of Argentine lamb. He didn't blink an eyelid and said, 'Oh, yes, well, that must be true then', and didn't demur at all that he had this Argentine lamb. Unfortunately all the 770 carcasses had been distributed by that time and used up. This particular butcher supplied Ellis with Argentine lamb. Ellis, thinking it was New Zealand lamb, used the bones for his dogs. The bones were fed to the dogs in the yard, outside the piggery. Sows were turned out from this piggery to be serviced on 17 October, and obviously were in contact and probably crunched up these bones. They showed symptoms on 21 October, and I think it was mentioned they were treated for arthritis. I don't know if a private veterinary surgeon was called in then, but on 25 October other pigs showed symptoms and that's when the disease was notified. So all you could say is that we had strong circumstantial evidence of the tie-up between establishment 1408 in Argentina, where we knew they had problems with diseased animals, and this particular Ellis case. Now an important, or interesting, factor of this consignment of 770 is that Argentine lamb was graded, in terms of quality, into three grades, designated by the colours of black, red and blue, (and I can't remember which is which). We looked at previous consignments, and normally there was 5 per cent of the lowest quality in a consignment.

This particular consignment had 16 per cent of low-quality carcasses. You can speculate that this particular butcher, with his financial problems, would probably have taken most of the lower-quality meat, and he also had a van delivery service, going round farms in the area, where he was in the habit of throwing bones out for dogs as well. In looking at all of these cases we went back over the subsequent cases in that area and there was pretty strong circumstantial evidence that up to 19 of these cases could have arisen from contaminated lamb bones from this butcher. We concluded there were probably 19 primaries immediately from this particular consignment. This report went to Tolworth, in December 1967, and was the subject of a White Paper that the CVO presented to Parliament.[92]

What we couldn't establish in questioning Ellis was whether he was committing an offence by using these bones, which had been exposed to pigs, unboiled.[93] He asserted, of course, that he had boiled them before feeding the dogs, which we had to accept, because we had no evidence to the contrary. In the report we could only say that the owner alleged that the bones were cooked before being given to the dogs. However, it was pretty obvious that they were not. In our opinion this was the origin of the infection and we probably had another 18 primary cases in the same area from the same consignment of meat. Then the whole meat question was extended and we looked at other importations from Argentina and from this establishment, and although the circumstantial evidence was weaker, it was concluded at the end that there was possibly up to 40 primary cases in the area and all the others were probably secondaries.

An amusing thing arising out of this is that we banned the importation of sheep meat immediately, of course, on this finding. The Argentines were up in arms about this accusation that they had introduced infection into this country. They sent a high-level delegation and sat in a hotel in London for three days. They didn't come near Oswestry, didn't go near Tolworth, and had a press conference

---

[92] Mr Fred Peart, the Minister for Agriculture Fisheries and Food, announced to the House of Commons on 21 December 1967 (*Hansard* 756, 1967–68, cols 1481–1491), that adequate resources would be made available to meet the current needs of agriculture and livestock in the Government's White Paper, *Annual Price Review and Determination 1968* (Cmnd 3558). The following year's policy document noted that 'the production of beef in 1968–69 was still suffering from the aftermath of the FMD epidemic and a fall of 3 per cent in the volume of net output was expected in the current farm year compared with 1967–68'. See MAFF (1969), quote on page 8. See also the Chief Veterinary Officer's report on the origin of the outbreak, Northumberland (1969a): Appendix 3, 115–117.

[93] The Diseases of Animals (Waste Foods) Order 1957 prohibited feeding of waste food to cattle, sheep, pigs, goats or poultry that contains, or has been in contact with, any part of a carcass. See Northumberland (1969a): Appendix 5, 127.

where they said they had no evidence that the disease had come from Argentina, and went home. And that was the end as far as they were concerned. But in March [1968] they asked for a delegation to come from this country, and Gwyn Beynon, Roger Macrae and Gregor Henderson[94] went to the four countries that had signed the Bledisloe Agreement with us in 1928, which gave conditions for the importation of beef into this country. They renegotiated the conditions for de-boned beef, refined later with the actual procedures for maturation and de-boning, but they also looked at the sheep problem and they agreed, subject to certain conditions, that we would allow the importation of sheep meat from Tierra del Fuego, Santa Cruz, and a province in Chile, subject to certain conditions that the sheep were born in those provinces. The notification of disease was a legal obligation, the animals should be slaughtered in frigorificos (slaughterhouses) that we approved, and the carcasses would then be kept for three months in deep freeze, before being exported to us. In the meantime there mustn't be any outbreaks of FMD in the area. Those were the amendments to the Bledisloe Agreement agreed at that time. I agree that there may have been a reduction in the incidence of the disease from these countries, but from then on we haven't had a case of FMD from South America, so I don't know whether it was the new arrangements for importation or reduction in incidence which was a major factor.

Morris: Just very briefly, if I could clarify a point Howard made, which lifts the responsibility [for diagnosis] from the practitioner. The farmer as I recall, had seen the pigs being stiff, showing signs of what he thought was rheumatism. A previous time he had the pigs treated with a salicylate by his vet and had asked the vet for some of that magic powder that worked before. He had administered the magic powder to the pigs, but of course they had FMD, and they didn't get better. That's when he called the veterinary practitioner who came to see them, and the practitioner actually reported it at once. The vet picked it up straight away.

Soulsby: In the 1967 outbreak there was no indication that any infection might have come from other than imported meat from Argentina.

Rees: Yes, Chairman. We looked at all the other possibilities, and I think somebody else has mentioned that you get letters from all sorts in these situations, I wouldn't like to call them cranks, but the letters suggested the origin of the outbreak in 1967, and I might remember one in particular. We had to take these seriously, on instruction of the Prime Minister [Harold Wilson, Labour]

---

[94] See note 83. For the visit of the Argentine delegation and revision of the Bledisloe Agreement, see TNA(PRO) MAF 276/396 and MAF 287/529.

that we had to reply to all these sensibly, although some were actually ludicrous. One of the suggestions was that the disease had come in from South America with salmon migrating across the Atlantic and up the Welsh rivers. This was a serious suggestion to us that this was the origin of the disease. We also had a look at the situation where there was a lot of disease in Germany at the time, 4000 outbreaks in 1967, and troops had come back to a depot near Wrexham from Germany around about the crucial time. We had to investigate the possibility that they brought the disease from Germany, but found no link at all. We did look at all the other possibilities, before we concluded that we had strong circumstantial evidence that the cause was the Argentine lamb bones being fed to dogs, going into pigs and triggering off the outbreak.[95]

Soulsby: One thing we haven't mentioned, which is not directly related to the meat question, but that's the role of birds in the spread of the disease. Any comments on that?

Rees: Yes. Another thing that worried us up at the Wrexham FMC depot was that these frozen carcasses were being cut up with an electric saw and there were piles of bone dust. The place was inundated with starlings, which were gleefully devouring this bonemeal, and would then fly off. Whether they caused any outbreaks around there, we don't know, but it was a possibility that the bonemeal could have been mechanically contaminated and taken out by the birds, but it was impossible to identify specific cases. There was a danger from the depot, because of the means used to cut up the carcasses.

Sellers: In the Gowers Report, there was a lot of talk about the birds bringing virus across from Holland and Belgium and so on.[96] The Danes, Swedes and Norwegians always said it wasn't the birds, because the virus went from Germany to those countries, but not at the time of the bird migration. The Meteorological Office under G W Hurst did some work on the bird flights over the years up to 1967 and found that there were wind sources there.[97] Later, after the 1981 epidemic, Alex Donaldson and I gave the Met Office a number of outbreaks on

---

[95] Other factors thought to be involved in the introduction and spread of FMD included imported animals, fresh, frozen and chilled meat and offal, bones, hooves and horns, semen, glandular products, hay and straw and vegetable matter, hides, passenger traffic, vehicular traffic, and the wind. The role of birds was also discussed in the Northumberland Report, noting that virus from the feet and feathers of birds was passed others experimentally as long as 91 hours after contact. See Northumberland (1969a): 12, 25 and Northumberland (1969b): 299.

[96] See Gowers (1954): 11–13 and 106–122.

[97] Hurst (1968a, b, c).

the south coast, which were said to be from birds. We also gave them some that we knew were meat, and they managed to pick out the ones that were due to birds as being caused by wind. Birds certainly can transfer virus, but it's more mechanical – on their feet, or by regurgitation of food that they have eaten.[98]

Richardson: One very quick, anecdotal point. The first case I saw this year was in housed cattle, where the farmer claimed that a flock of starlings had roosted in the first affected building seven days prior to the animals becoming sick.

Soulsby: I think there are two more sessions to do, but now we come to the Northumberland Committee and we have a member of that Committee here this afternoon, Henry Plumb.

Plumb: Thank you very much, Chairman. I think I can be fairly brief on the details of the Northumberland Committee, because it has become apparent as the discussion this afternoon has worn on that most of you here at the seminar are completely *au fait* with the findings in that report, or at least the major findings. May I therefore just pick up two points from the discussions that have taken place so far? The first is a reference to imports, but in particular to swill feeding. I would condemn it and I did at the time in 1967 and in 1969. Recently I looked at my notes and over a ten-year period from 1954 to 1965, there were 200 cases of FMD and 110 were on swill-fed premises. At that time, of course, there was no law that said that the product had to be cooked. It now does, but is it?[99] To suggest that you can't get rid of the product that goes into the swill feed is a bit of a nonsense, when you think that everything over 30 months of age goes into an incinerator because of BSE, and therefore it should be possible to handle it in a totally different way.

The second thing is the question of the publicity, saying that there was no adverse publicity in 1967. There was. The headline in the farming papers was 'Sack Plumb said the butchers'.[100] The reason for that headline was they [the butchers] accused me at the time of being biased. I appeared before the butchers and I told them I was, because that was the truth. I was put on the [Northumberland] Committee and therefore served as an independent with the rest of the marvellous team under the Duke of Northumberland. We were able to come to a conclusion.

---

[98] See also Kaleta (2002).

[99] See note 93.

[100] See Plumb (2001): 51.

There was a minority report,[101] and it wasn't mine, I still have my minority report. I had written it in the event of the introduction of blanket vaccination, which was being discussed at the time. Had we come out with blanket vaccination, I would have produced a minority report against it, for the simple reason that had we vaccinated on an annual basis, and then inevitably a live vaccine as we knew it then would be taken back into the hills, and there would be 30 or 40 sheep left in crevices on the hills with the possibility that they would immediately get it [the virus]. Ring vaccination is of course a totally different thing. We naturally talk about the importance of maintaining a ban on the import of meat, mutton, lamb and pig meat, particularly from countries, or areas of countries where FMD is endemic. We said that a ban on the import of meat coming from those countries should continue. It's interesting to note at the moment, if my figures are correct, that in the last two years we imported 37 000 tons of pig meat and over 100 000 tons of beef from 26 countries where FMD exists. That, I think, speaks for itself. We have been sitting on a volcano, a time bomb, call it what you will, over this period.

We said that there should be a complete ban on all imports from countries, or areas of countries, where FMD is endemic, because of the high risk of introducing FMD into Great Britain from imported carcass and beef offal on strictly animal health grounds. As we have just heard, we said as far as the beef was concerned, 'Take the bones out, let it come in a Cryovac pack[102] and we believe it will be safe'. That has been successful since we have had no further outbreaks that we can claim have come from South America. The South American farmers were pretty concerned at the time that this was so, and I and others spent quite a bit of time in Argentina and Brazil, in Paraguay, Uruguay and so on. I had some doubts about the efficacy of the vaccine that was being produced in some of those areas. We did visit many stations and we did establish both in the frigorificos (slaughterhouses) and on the estancias where the lamb had come from. It is quite remarkable at that time we were able to establish the lamb's origin. Incidentally, on that point as the Duke himself said at the beginning, I think quoting views that the virus had come in, or was alleged to have come in through imported meat for swill fed to pigs, my understanding – my recollection – is that at that time we did in fact find the family where the meat had been bought, and the bone

---

[101] See Northumberland (1969a): Dissenting Note by Anthony Cripps, QC, 97–100, which recommended immediate application of ring vaccination in any outbreak.

[102] Lord Plumb wrote: 'A Cryovac pack was meat, with the bones removed, sealed in a plastic pack and was introduced into meat processing in 1969.' Note on draft transcript, 2 June 2003.

presumably carried by a dog across a field of cattle in Oswestry. It was quite interesting that we were able to trace it back to the estancia in Argentina. So the recommendations were made and following the report we were very pleased to note that the Government followed those recommendations almost to the letter. I have to say that is what we haven't done on this occasion and while you don't want to dwell on that, I know, nevertheless one Minister said to me fairly recently the only thing we didn't do was bring in the army at the right time.[103]

Well, I submit the only thing they didn't do was take action at the right time, which would have made a difference. But I'll finish with one more point, because it was the major point of the whole of the Northumberland deliberations and the timings that we reached. That was if we continued to import products from countries where the disease was endemic, or even where it exists, then we must prepare for the possibility of another outbreak. In preparation for that possibility we should prepare immediately for ring vaccination. Therefore, I think, as has already been said this afternoon, if we did have another outbreak the public wouldn't wear it in the way that we have had to handle it in the past. On the question of slaughter and ring vaccination I am pleased to note that in Pirbright and elsewhere in the world, there are various preparations for a vaccine that could operate on a ring-type basis. Certainly I would object most strongly to an annual vaccination such as they have or have had in Argentina, and are now having to revert to. We have a totally different situation here in the mix of meat animals and different types of farming; it just wouldn't work in the same way.

Chairman, one could go on for a long time on that Report, which took evidence from 1000 people, with over 10 000 letters, some of them very cranky indeed. Many letters were passed back to the Ministry. We had a marvellous team and I just wish Bill Weipers and the Duke of Northumberland could be here to listen to the discussion that's taking place here this afternoon.

Meldrum: May I deal with the swill issue first of all. Following the Northumberland Committee, I was given the job in 1972 of helping to revise the arrangements. Quite clearly, at that time the swill plant standards were absolutely abysmal, it was a local authority second-tier function and everybody in the field knew that they were absolutely abysmal. This is from memory now – we had about 6300 or so swill plants prior to 1973. The first tranche of licensing [to tighten hygiene standards] in April 1973 cut down the swill plants to 4500 and when full standards were imposed the number [of swill plants] came

---

[103] See note 116.

down at the rate of knots, so that the end result was a very significant reduction. We are now down to about 90 swill plants at the moment, and although standards were significantly raised, there were other instructions in place in the field, such as checking on swill-fed pigs on a routine basis, particularly if there appeared to be an FMD threat to the UK from overseas through importation of meat. Not only did they have their pigs inspected, but they were advised of the threat from overseas and that they should be on their guard, and were told what to look for and to report any suspicions to the local DVO. Whether that happened earlier this year, I do not know, and we shan't know until that court case is heard.[104] Those were the plans in place.

Quite clearly the importation issue that Henry Plumb mentioned, is very pertinent, and it is quite clear that up until about 1993, I think, Jim [Morris], we did have a very tight import policy on importation, probably the tightest in the whole EU, particularly for lamb and bone-in beef. We had a very tight policy and that was gradually eroded over time by the Standing Veterinary Committee (SVC)[105] who were more interested in a flexible approach to imports from developing countries, which made it particularly difficult for us. When the EU expanded to 15 countries [in 1995], to an extent whereby the UK, Ireland and Denmark no longer formed a blocking minority in the SVC, things went downhill, and it is absolutely true that we are now importing meat into the EU, sometimes without detailed border checks, from areas that we would not have considered acceptable after the Northumberland Report in 1969. There should be checks on meat coming in from developing countries. I question whether or not these [checks] are thorough and certainly they are not within the EU. One further point on post-Northumberland contingency planning; we put in place not only contingency plans for trained staff in what to do if there were to be an outbreak, but also the details were already drawn up for ring vaccination. We had exercises in every division. We also worked with the Pirbright laboratory, which had a mobile laboratory that would go to an area of high risk, so that samples of milk could be taken from neighbouring dairy herds, tested overnight for the presence of virus, so that if found the herd could be killed immediately.

---

[104] Northumberland County Council won the case against the owner of the farm where the first case of FMD was discovered in 2001. See Anon. (2002): 735.

[105] For example, a Standing Veterinary Committee press release, dated 4 April 2001, reported the favourable discussions of EC proposals of protective measures against FMD in the UK, Ireland, France and The Netherlands, an agreement on an EC proposal for vaccination of zoo animals against FMD and a review of FMD in some developing countries. See europa.eu.int/comm/dgs/health_consumer/library/press/press126_en.html (visited 19 June 2003).

Those plans were already in place. I have heard nothing recently whatsoever about testing milk, but those plans were in place earlier.

Finally, one of the critical issues, and in the Northumberland recommendations, is on staffing levels. For the record, it is obviously axiomatic that the problems this year are partly related to the lack of veterinary staff in the SVS, not only veterinary officers, but senior veterinary staff in particular, because the whole layer of deputy regional veterinary officers, was abolished post-Lebrecht Report.[106] I don't particularly want to get into that, except that it causes me a great deal of anguish even now, but I do have in front of me a report that was put up to the Permanent Secretary in February 1995 when the new staffing levels were being discussed, post-Lebrecht – there had already been a significant reduction in veterinary staff because of Treasury and ministerial pressures. I did say that if this report was accepted and implemented that we would be short of senior staff in the field to direct operations and senior veterinary staff at Tolworth would have to be drafted into the field to take control. I was confident that we could deal with a minor emergency, with the proposed new structure, but anything more serious could present a significant problem to senior managers in the veterinary field service.

Rees: Thank you, Chairman. I will take up the issue of the vaccine bank[107] that arose out of the Northumberland recommendations. Before that I would like to read a summary of a paper which was sent to Northumberland on the origin and the characteristics of the virus we were dealing with in 1967. It makes interesting reading:

> ...this virus had an unusual capacity for spread, it was highly diffusable, it had an unusual ability to persist, it was difficult to disinfect against, early excretion before overt disease normally 24 to 48 hours, but Pirbright showed that it could be up to five days.[108]

---

[106] Mr Angus Taylor wrote: 'The Lebrecht management review completely destroyed the middle management of the SVS and in 2001 there were not sufficient field DVOs available to take control of smaller centres that should have been set up in Devon and Cumberland.' Note on draft transcript, 19 May 2003. See also Lebrecht and Corner (1993).

[107] See Northumberland (1969b) and note 20.

[108] Dr Bob Sellers wrote: 'Further investigations on the characteristics of different strains of FMD virus showed that the strain responsible for the 1967–68 outbreak, O_1, was not unusual, but fell within the normal range.' Note on draft transcript, 15 August 2002. See Table 2 above, reproduced from Northumberland (1969a): 54, paras 84 and 85, and Northumberland (1969b): 43, para 225.

This is the important one – sheep showed typical fulminating disease in some areas, in other areas they didn't, but even when sheep were severely affected, there was little or no spread of disease from that source. I think the Northumberland Report mentioned that some serological surveys were carried out and positive antibodies were found in some sheep,[109] but it was decided to do nothing about them and they were left and didn't spread disease. The last point was that the virus did not readily infect pigs. Of the 98 570 slaughtered only 327 showed lesions. This puts the different importance of these species into perspective.[110]

Following the recommendation in the Northumberland Report, a vaccine bank[111] was set up containing 1.5 million doses of liquid vaccine of A, O and C strains, ready to be used. It was stored in three cold stores scattered throughout the country, but the difficulty was that this vaccine had a shelf-life of between 12 and 18 months. After 12 months it was tested by Pirbright to check the potency, and if it deteriorated it had to be replaced.

There were three storage depots. Equipment for vaccination was held at Weybridge, so all the preparations for vaccination *à la* Northumberland were put in place. This was a very expensive operation and by the time I became CVO in 1980 the cost to us was £700 000 a year to maintain this bank, and we, of course, never used it, and hopefully never would use it. As Keith mentioned, we were being pressed, as usual, to cut our staff to save costs, so rather than cut staff I wanted to do something about this bank of vaccine. I discussed it with six other countries – Australia, New Zealand, Ireland, Finland, Denmark, Norway and Sweden – who all maintained a stamping-out policy without vaccination, a similar policy to ours, and we agreed to set up an international bank of concentrated antigen held under low temperature over liquid nitrogen. This was agreed by the seven countries to share the costs. We then went out to tender to

---

[109] Experimental work at Pirbright during 1967–68 found that cattle and sheep could be sources of infection for up to five days (ten days with pigs) before clinical symptoms appeared. The virus is destroyed by heat, direct sunlight and certain disinfectants, but thrives in cold and darkness. Laboratory tests showed that the virus can survive, under favourable conditions, for 14 days on wool, four weeks on cow hair, 11 weeks on boot leather, 14 weeks on rubber boots and 15 weeks on hay. Northumberland (1969a): 114.

[110] Pirbright summarized the general epidemiological position for the Northumberland Committee: 'Sheep act as maintenance hosts, pigs as amplifiers and cattle as indicators'. Northumberland (1969b): 94.

[111] See note 16; for discussions on contingency plans for future FMD vaccination, see TNA(PRO) MAF 287/479/1 and 287/479/2.

all the manufacturers with the protocols and I think, Noel, we stipulated that you had to have a PD50 of at least 10 at that time. We introduced four strains initially, the A_{22} Iraq, A_{24} Cruzeiro, O_1 Lausanne and C_1 Oberbayern, stored at a specially renovated building at Pirbright,[112] which cost us £170 000 to renovate, and the vaccine initially cost us about £240 000. We, along with Australia, had a drawing right of 500 000 cattle doses. New Zealand had 300 000, and the other four countries had rights of 100 000 each. Each country paid for the bank *pro rata* to their drawing rights, which brought our annual costs down from £700 000 to £30 000. However we didn't really get much credit from the politicians for this saving, but at least they didn't reduce the staff. This bank has been in existence since 1985, when we signed the international treaty establishing the bank. We had difficulties with the treaty because unfortunately the lawyers in all seven countries were involved in discussing the drafts, and every time we sent it round somebody would change one or two words which meant that it all had to be sent round again. So after about five circulations, we said, 'That's enough, it's not going around again, you either agree or get out of it'. So they agreed and it was signed by the Ministers in 1985. Now as far as I know the potency of this vaccine has been maintained and is tested regularly – it used to be tested every three years through cattle and every year through guinea-pigs. It has proved to be a valuable and cost-effective bank which is there for emergency use when necessary and hopefully, in our view, it would never be used. It satisfied the Northumberland recommendation that we have a bank of vaccine available.

Soulsby: Can I just ask you one thing on that, Howard? Is there a hierarchy of potential strains of virus that you might anticipate and hence make vaccines from, and others that you would not bother with?

Rees: Yes, we had this facility at Pirbright, who were taking samples from all over the world, so we knew exactly where the dangers existed, and although we used four strains to start with, we added an additional one in 1986 and some others have been added subsequently, such as A_{15} Thailand, based on the advice from Pirbright, and also of interest to Australia, who are particularly concerned in the Far East. So the range of strains to be held would be determined by Pirbright.

---

[112] 'The international FMD vaccine bank', undated document. Details supplied by Mr Howard Rees. For details of vaccine banks and recent outbreaks, see Forman and Garland (2002).

Mowat: Economically, it's a very good proposition, because what is in fact stored is the purified viral antigen and there is provision also for rapidly formulating this antigen into the finished product that can be used in the field. The storage life of liquid nitrogen-stored antigen is extremely long, so it's very economic from that point of view.

Garland: A couple of comments on that. A number of other vaccine banks have been set up since that time. The European vaccine bank, of which we are also a member, the North American vaccine bank, and there's one in South America. Strains have now been tested for at least 13 years and shown to maintain potency, that is the antigen stored over liquid nitrogen, so I think one could say that their stable shelf-life would be indefinite. The most recent recommendation from the World Reference Laboratory includes 17 different vaccine strains, classified into three levels of outbreak risk: high, medium and low. The vaccine bank is able to formulate either aqueous aluminium hydroxide saponin vaccines, which are good for ruminants, but also oil vaccines that are good for ruminants and pigs. An emergency vaccine would almost certainly go for an oil vaccine if one was able to do that. There are however some complications in terms of liability, and particularly in terms of deciding when to activate that bank.[113]

Soulsby: Any other comments? I have an anecdotal comment about sources of the infection coming from overseas. I mentioned that I was on an Animal Committee of the National Science Foundation in the USA and we were concerned with the importation of dangerous pathogens, both human and animal. We went round many institutions, including the US Customs. We got to Chicago, where of course there were many illegal importations of meat and meat products from central and eastern Europe. As you know as you go into the USA the customs declaration form says you can't import meat or meat products. So we asked the customs officials how many illegal importations they had and they said, 'Oh, we get lots and confiscate the whole lot'. Then we asked, 'What do you do with them?' They replied, 'We put them in the ice box and keep them there'. I asked, 'What do you do after that?' He said, 'Well, we get rid of them'. I said, 'Into an incinerator?' He replied, 'No, we put them in the garbage'. And the garbage goes to pigs. I think that merely points out that the mystery is not that we get these highly infectious diseases, but that we don't get many more of them. Let's now go on to our final point, the aftermath, and Abigail Woods is going to wrap it up.

---

[113] For background to the disease, see Sellers (1984).

Woods: We have already discussed various points I was going to raise here, so I am not going to speak for very long. The main problem after the Northumberland Committee, of course, was for MAFF to decide how much of that report it was going to accept, for, of course, MAFF reserved the right to look at the political and economic questions of FMD itself. I think part of that consideration arose from a political sensitivity in blaming Argentina for the outbreak. I got that impression from looking at the sources [at the Public Record Office, Kew] that MAFF was very concerned that the Northumberland Committee might come out and say, 'Ban all Argentine meat', and then it would have had to answer to Argentina, which, of course, responded to the three-month meat ban by stopping the purchase of all British export goods – apparently about £20 million was lost.[114] There was also the vaccination question: how much of the vaccination recommendations were MAFF going to accept. And I have seen the draft of the Minister's speech to Parliament, how he was going to respond to the Northumberland Committee Report. One or two of these drafts has actually omitted to accept ring vaccination and one or two little comments in the margin say, 'Well, I think if we have a proper import policy we don't need to bother about vaccination'.[115] Obviously the suggestion was thrown out, because the final draft did accept vaccination, although I think at that time it was actually estimated that it would cost £1 million a year and the Treasury was not happy about that one. So it's interesting to hear from you about that the actual outcome was the vaccine bank. From the farming perspective, it seems that various schemes were launched on a nationwide basis, to try to help the affected farmers to restock, but again MAFF's scheme that was introduced was to try to prevent them restocking all at once, which of course would push the prices up, as there weren't enough cattle to go round. There were various subsidies to farmers to delay restocking and to plough up instead, although I believe there were problems getting farmers to accept that, simply because in Cheshire it wasn't always possible to plant arable crops instead of continuing with dairy cattle. It seems that in the years following 1967 the level of anxiety about the possibility of the disease coming back gradually reduced, up until the scare in 1981. But since then FMD has fallen off the agenda. Certainly for my generation of veterinary students it really wasn't anything. I think we were shown a film, but

---

[114] For details of the Argentine reaction to the British trade embargo, see TNA(PRO) FCO 7/168 and 7/1070. For details of policy discussions following the Northumberland Committee Report, see TNA(PRO) FCO 67/71, 67/72, 67/73.

[115] See TNA(PRO) MAF 276/403.

Figure 14: Restocking plans discussed following the 1967 FMD epidemic. L to R: Tom Stobo, Henry Plumb and Mary Brancker.

that was the limit of our education on FMD; it was history. Obviously this year is going to provoke quite a few rethinks on that one.[116]

Soulsby: Is there any social report on how farmers got back to normal? Was it a long time that it took them to accommodate to the loss of animals and restocking?

Woods: I am not sure about that, to be honest. I believe the state of farming was in quite good shape then, so farmers were probably more likely to go back and restock than they are today.

Plumb: They didn't have the milk or livestock quota restrictions we have today. You only had to go to market and buy some cattle. A lot did restock and a lot improved their stocks by doing so. I remember one farmer in particular who said he had stepped some ten years forward by buying some pedigree stock that he now felt that he could afford, from the stock that he had before. So in times of adversity things [progress] did happen.

Taylor: After the FMD outbreak of 1967–68 we had a big importation of Holstein cattle from Canada. I think about 500 came in. I have a record that one

[116] The Committee of Public Accounts Report noted that some aspects of the handling of the 2001 outbreak were 'inexcusable', such as the absence of a vaccination policy and the failure to bring in the military at an earlier stage (day 25 compared with day 12 in 1967). The cost to the public sector was estimated at over £3 billion and over £5 billion to the private sector, with tourism losing most. Other points included the lack of contingency planning for any more than ten premises being infected and the narrow application of measures, directed towards agriculture at the expense of other local industries, such as tourism; a national movement ban could have been introduced from day one; the countryside kept open without blanket closure of footpaths; and senior administrators brought in earlier to take charge of local disease. Lessons from the 1967–68 outbreak, such as use of the armed forces, seem to have 'fallen out of the collective memory of the Department…due to a narrow outlook and a lack of contextual awareness'. See Public Accounts (2003). For criteria to trigger EU emergency vaccination plans in future outbreaks, see EU (1999).

farm in Cheshire that was able to restock eight weeks after disinfection had been completed. I am very puzzled at the moment as to why it has taken so long in the present epidemic for people to restock,[117] because they didn't seem to have that difficulty in Cheshire. Ken Tyrrell may remember it better than I do, but I don't think we had a great problem. The NFU set up a register of people who had stock for sale and this was a great help to the farmers when it came to restocking.

Tyrrell: Angus is quite right. Those Canadian Holsteins came in, but there were also a lot that came from Scotland. The farmers unfortunately were under pressure to get a milk cheque going and they often turned round and bought in a lot of brucellosis problems.

There is one question that I would like to ask my colleagues here. The Government has said, through their Ministers this year, that regulations were relaxed too soon in the 1967–68 outbreak. That's not my recollection. My recollection is that we allowed a certain amount of restocking to take place under controlled conditions,[118] and there was recrudescence. It was not that regulations were relaxed too soon. I think this has just been put on so that they can continue at present, or up until recently, holding farmers under restrictions far longer than we would consider a veterinary necessity.

Meldrum: It's absolutely right. I remember having to go back to Crewe to re-disinfect farms, because this trial restocking under controlled conditions had indicated that there was still virus present. In particular we had to re-fumigate grain and spray haystacks with formalin to ensure that any residual virus was removed.

Chairman, may I pick up just one or two more points from the Northumberland Committee Report. Questions are often asked why burial is still not taking place on farms. Well, it's BSE related. Advice is that carcasses containing the brain and spinal cord should not be buried. It's simply a reflection of the concerns within the agriculture department on BSE and advice from the Spongiform

---

[117] Mr Angus Taylor wrote: 'There appeared to be much more political interference in 2001 and the 20-day movement restrictions imposed on farmers after the outbreak appeared to be draconian and not necessary from a veterinary point of view – 14 days would have been sufficient initially.' Note on draft transcript, 19 May 2003.

[118] Mr Ken Tyrrell wrote: 'Restocking in this context allowed for the movement on to a farm of, say, ten bullocks for a period of three to four weeks with frequent inspections. If FMD did not occur in these cattle then all restocking restrictions were removed. Eighteen recrudescences occurred: four in Cheshire, two in Staffordshire, two in Shropshire, two in Flintshire, one in Denbighshire and one in Worcestershire, plus six cases where it spread to neighbouring farms.' Note on draft transcript, 20 May 2003. See Northumberland (1969a): 42, para 70.

Encephalopathy Advisory Committee (SEAC). So rendering (pressure heat treatment) took place and that in itself raises additional problems.

One or two things though from the Northumberland Report were not picked up. Lime was mentioned in the context of burial. I don't think lime has ever been used in pits. I think most of us would agree that you shouldn't use lime, because it preserves the carcasses, so we would not follow that suggestion. We haven't discussed milk.[119] To Angus surely and also to Ken, one of the biggest problems we had in Cheshire was disease following the milk tanker, from farm to farm, due to evacuation of air from the back of the tank when there was infected milk on board – I think Bob Sellers is making a rude noise in my direction that indicates dissent.[120] Be that as it may, there is still a provision in place that milk tanker drivers should put an air filter on their vehicle in an infected area. I think that has been practised recently, but it took an awful long time to put in place. Another point to mention about firearms, about pistols. In the old days Angus [Taylor] said we went to farms carrying a pistol, I think these have been withdrawn from the field since I retired four and a half years ago, for health and safety, or safety reasons. A pity though, because in the old days when you went to a farm, all the affected stock were killed on the spot, that day, and the rest were killed maybe the next morning. Any animals with lesions were put down straight away that evening, or whenever you were there. The Northumberland Report said that a vet should be in charge of the centre. That did not happen recently. It also says that there should be no reports made to Tolworth, to headquarters, when a vet visits a farm to examine a suspect case. That recommendation was not implemented, and up until this year any animal that was believed to have disease, be it this or any other notifiable disease, would have to be reported and discussed with a vet in Tolworth. I believe that to be a very useful safeguard. I do actually remember, by the way, cases that were referred back from Tolworth to the field, correctly, for a second opinion. I also recollect we had a problem with a particular diagnostic procedure at Pirbright, way after this report was written, so mistakes can occur. We have to be very careful that the right decision is made on the right grounds. It also says in the report that ministers should have new powers, additional powers, to ensure that all their controls are supported in

---

[119] See 'Extracts from the Milk Code of Practice as prepared in 1969 by MAFF', Northumberland (1969b): Appendix 3, 121–129.

[120] Dr Bob Sellers wrote: 'Experimental investigations at that time at the Micobiological Research Establishment, Porton, Wiltshire, in which *Bacillus globigii* spores were added to the milk in a tanker, showed that the number of spores recovered when the vented air was sampled was a very small proportion of those present in milk. It was concluded that ground contamination was a more likely route of dissemination of FMD virus than air-borne spread.' Note on draft transcript, 15 August 2002. See Donaldson (1997).

legislation. Quite clearly, that was not the case recently and that's why the Animal Health Bill has now been pushed through the House of Commons in an awful hurry.[121] Lastly on artificial insemination (AI), there was a very useful comment in the report about DIY AI, which has been picked up recently, and practised successfully in affected areas – that is farmers doing their own cattle insemination with their own equipment, using a proper syringe which deposits semen in the vagina or lower part of the cervix. That has actually worked extremely well.[122]

Rees: Just a quick one, in the 1967 outbreak essentially the first phase of it finished in February 1968, followed by a 25-day period of freedom, and then 24 recrudescences of disease. Eighteen farms had the disease for the second time, but only 12 of them were true recrudescences and the opinion at the time was that it was due to contaminated hay, which was difficult to disinfect. As a rule of thumb infected premises were cleared four weeks after the completion of disinfection, or six weeks after the completion of slaughter, whichever was the sooner, but in the case of the outbreaks in 1967–68, farms were released in groups, because there were many contiguous farms. They were allowed to restock to 50 per cent initially, and if they were healthy after two weeks, then they were permitted to complete restocking.

Soulsby: Right, we have one minute and I think I will use that minute, unless there's any other pertinent comment about this, to say that I think we have had a good afternoon, we have had lots of discussions, and all that remains for me to say is thank you all very much for coming along and participating. It will all be put in writing because it's all been taped, and you will get an opportunity to see what you have said, and to correct it in a minor way, but you can't rewrite your speech. Now I will invite you to go for informal drinks.

Tansey: Before we do that, may I add the thanks of the History of Twentieth Century Medicine Group to you all for providing not only an entertaining and educational afternoon, but it has been a great privilege to listen to your reminiscences and I would like to ask you to thank our Chairman, Lord Soulsby, for his excellent chairing of this session. Thank you very much.

---

[121] See note 42.

[122] Restocking in 1967–68 was helped by the DIY AI breeding programme that continued to operate using semen from the Milk Marketing Board's Artificial Insemination Centres. Disposable syringes of semen were delivered to the farm gate in response to a telephone call. About 50 per cent of the 30 000 inseminations were successful. See Whitlock (1968): 105. Mr Keith Meldrum wrote: 'This was necessary because personnel trained in AI were not permitted to visit farms to inseminate cattle.' Note on draft transcript, 17 June 2003. See also O'Sullivan (1971).

References

Anon. (n.d.a) *FMD: Report of veterinary mission to the South American countries covered by the Bledisloe Agreement of 1928, 19 March–17 April 1968.*

Anon. (n.d.b) *Northumberland Committee of Inquiry into the 1967–68 Outbreak: Applicability of recommendations during the 2001 outbreak.* See www.defra.gov.uk/corporate/inquiries/lessons/fmdapplic.pdf (visited 11 February 2003).

Anon. (n.d.c) *Wildy Report: Consideration of option 4. MAFF's Need for Pirbright.* Papers provided by Howard Rees.

Anon. (1926) Foot and mouth disease. *British Medical Journal* **i**: 1002.

Anon. (2002) News and Reports: DEFRA welcomes FMD verdicts. *Veterinary Record* **150**: 735.

(Auditor General) Comptroller and Auditor General. (2002) *The 2001 Outbreak of FMD.* HC939, Session 2001–02. London: HMSO and from www.nao.gov.uk/publications/nao_reports/01-02/0102939.pdf (visited 8 April 2003).

Beck E, Strohmaier K. (1987) Subtyping of European FMD virus strains by nucleotide sequence determination. *Journal of Virology* **61**: 1621–1629.

van Bekkum J G, Frenkel H S, Fredericks H H, Frenkel S. (1959) Observations on the carrier state of cattle exposed to FMD virus. *Tijdschrift voor Diergeneeskunde* **84**: 1159–1164.

Berger J, Schermbrucker C G, Pay T W F. (1975) The immune response obtained with quadrivalent FMD vaccines in Kenyan cattle. *Bulletin – Office International des Epizooties* **83**: 327–336.

Bittle J L, Houghten R A, Alexander H, Shinnick T M, Sutcliffe J G, Lerner R A, Rowlands D J, Brown F. (1982) Protection against FMD by immunization with a chemically-synthesized peptide predicted from the viral nucleotide sequence. *Nature* **298**: 30–33.

Blancou J. (2002) History of the control of FMD. *Comparative Immunology, Microbiology and Infectious Diseases* **25**: 283–296.

Boothroyd J C, Highfield P E, Cross G A M, Rowlands D J, Lowe P A, Brown F, Harris T J R. (1981) Molecular cloning of FMD virus genome and nucleotide sequences in the structural protein genes. *Nature* **290**: 800–802.

Brooksby J B. (1967) FMD – a world problem. *Nature* **213**: 120–122. Delivered to the Royal Veterinary College, London, on 20 November 1966 on the difficulties of control by vaccines and published during the January 1967 outbreak.

Brooksby J B. (1974) *Animal Virus Research Institute 1924–1974.* Woking, Surrey: Pirbright.

Brooksby J B. (1981a) Genetic engineering and FMD vaccines. *Nature* **289**: 535.

Brooksby J B. (1981b) Tracing outbreaks of FMD. *Nature* **293**: 431–432.

Brown F, Crick J. (1959) Application of gel diffusion analysis to a study of the antigenic structure of inactivated vaccines prepared from the virus of FMD. *Journal of Immunology* **82**: 444–447.

Brown F. (2003) The history of research in FMD. *Virus Research* **91**: 3–7.

Capstick P B, Telling R C, Chapman W G, Stewart D L. (1962) Growth of a cloned strain of hamster kidney cells in suspended cultures and their susceptibility to the virus of FMD. *Nature* **195**: 1163–1164.

Chick H, Hume M, MacFarlane M. (1971) *War on Diseases: A history of the Lister Institute.* London: A Deutsch.

Donaldson A I, Doel T R. (1992) FMD: The risk for Great Britain after 1992. *Veterinary Record* **131**: 114–120.

Donaldson A I. (1997) Risks of spreading FMD through milk and dairy products. *Revue Scientifique et Technique – Office Internationale des Epizooties* **16**: 117–124.

European Commission. (1989) *Policies Currently Applied by Member States in the Control of FMD*. Report from the Commission to the Council on a study carried out by the Commission, SEC (89) 1731 final. Brussels: CEC.

European Union, Scientific Committee on Animal Health and Animal Welfare. (1999) *Report: Strategy for Emergency Vaccination against FMD*. Available from europa.eu.int/comm/food/fs/sc/scah/out22_en.pdf (visited 30 June 2003).

Fleming G. (1871) *Animal Plagues*. London: Chapman and Hall.

Forman A J, Garland A J M. (2002) FMD: The future of vaccine banks. *Revue Scientifique et Technique – Internationale Office of Epizootics* **21**: 601–612.

Frenkel H S. (1947) La culture de la virus de la fièvre aphteuse sur l'épithélium de la langue des bovides. *Bulletin – Office Internationale des Epizooties* **28**: 155–162.

(Gowers Report) Ministry of Agriculture and Fisheries (MAF). (1954) *Report of the Departmental Committee on FMD, 1952–54*. Cmnd 9214. London: HMSO. Sir Ernest Arthur Gowers, Chairman.

Henderson W M. (1954) The nature of FMD, in Gowers (1954): Appendix II, 91.

Herniman K A J, Medhurst P M, Wilson J N, Sellers R F. (1973) The action of heat, chemicals and disinfectants on swine vesicular disease virus. *Veterinary Record* **93**: 620–624.

Hughes H, Jones J O. (1969) *Plague on the Cheshire Plain: An account of the great foot and mouth epidemic, 1967–68*. London: Dennis Dobson.

Hurst G W. (1968a) *The Possibility of Continental Sources of FMD in England in Epidemics of October 1967 and Several Other Years*. Agricultural Memorandum No. 225. Bracknell: Meteorological Office [also in *Veterinary Record* **82**: 610–614].

Hurst G W. (1968b) *Addendum to Agricultural Memorandum No. 225*. Agricultural Memorandum No. 230.

Hurst G W. (1968c) *Possible Continental Origin of FMD – Rainfall distribution at start and end of trajectories.* Agricultural Memorandum No. 239.

Kaleta E F. (2002) FMD: Susceptibility of domestic poultry and free-living birds to infection and to disease – a review of the historical and current literature concerning the role of birds in spread of FMD viruses. *Deutsche tierarztliche Wochenschrift* **190**: 381–420.

Kitching R P. (1998) A recent history of FMD. *Journal of Comparative Pathology* **118**: 89–108.

Knowles N J, Samuel A R, Davies P R, Kitching R P, Donaldson A I. (2001) Outbreak of FMD virus serotype O in the UK caused by a pandemic strain. *Veterinary Record* **148**: 258–259.

Knowles N J, Davies P R, Samuel A R. (2002) A FMD pandemic reaches the UK. Fifty-sixth Annual Conference of the Association of Veterinary Teachers and Research Workers (AVTRW), Scarborough, 25–27 March 2002. *Research in Veterinary Science* 72 (suppl. A): 12–34.

Lebrecht A J, Corner D M. (1993–94) *Management Review of Animal Health and Veterinary Group*, Stages 1, 2 and 3 Report Review. Unpublished. The Stage Three Report, dated January 1994, is available at www.bseinquiry.gov.uk/files/mb/m25/tab03.pdf (visited 28 July 2003).

Leforban Y. (1999) Prevention measures against FMD in Europe in recent years. *Vaccine* 17: 1755–1759.

Leforban Y, Gerbier G. (2002) Review of the status of FMD and approach to control/eradication in Europe and Central Asia. *Revue Scientifique et Technique – Internationale Office of Epizootics* 21: 477–492.

Ministry of Agriculture, Fisheries and Food (MAFF). (1965) *Animal Health: Centenary 1865–1965.* London: HMSO.

MAFF. (1968) 'Background to the disease and history of infection and control in GB', Note by MAFF, March 1968. (MAFF/CI/1, NC(MAFF)(68)1).

MAFF. (1969) *Annual Price Review and Determination 1969.* Cmnd 3965. London: HMSO.

MAFF. (1970) *Animal Disease: FMD. Report on the animal health services in Great Britain.* London: HMSO.

Mowat G N, Chapman W G. (1962) Growth of FMD virus in a fibroblastic cell derived from hamster kidneys. *Nature* **194**: 253–255.

Mowat G N, Garland A J, Spier R E. (1978) The development of FMD vaccines. *Veterinary Record* **102**: 190–193.

(Northumberland Report) MAFF. (1969a) *Report of the Departmental Committee of Inquiry on FMD, 1968. Part One.* Cmnd 3999. London: HMSO. The Duke of Northumberland, Chairman.

(Northumberland Report) MAFF. (1969b) *Report of the Departmental Committee of Inquiry on FMD, 1968. Part Two.* Cmnd 4225. London: HMSO. The Duke of Northumberland, Chairman.

O'Sullivan K. (1971) The organization of a farmers' "do-it-yourself" bovine insemination service. *Veterinary Record* **88**: 190–193.

(Phillips Report) House of Commons. (2000) *The BSE Inquiry: The inquiry into BSE and variant CJD in the UK.* HC887 (1999–2000). London: Stationery Office. Lord Phillips, Chairman.

Plumb H. (2001) *The Plumb Line: A journey through agriculture and politics.* London: The Greycoat Press.

Power A P, Harris S A. (1973) A cost–benefit evaluation of alternative control policies for FMD in Great Britain. *Journal of Agricultural Economics* **24**: 573–600.

(Pretyman Report) MAF. (1922) *Report of the Departmental Committee Appointed to Consider the Outbreak of FMD, 1922.* Cmnd 1784. London: HMSO. Captain the Right Hon. E G Pretyman, MP, Chairman.

(Pretyman Report) MAF. (1925) *Report of the Departmental Committee Appointed to Consider the Outbreak of FMD which occurred in 1923–24.* Cmnd 2350. London: HMSO. Captain the Right Hon. E G Pretyman, Chairman.

(Public Accounts) Committee of Public Accounts. (2003) *Fifth Report: The 2001 outbreak of FMD.* HC 487, Session 2002–03. See DEFRA's draft contingency plan on www.defra.gov.uk/animalh/diseases/fmd/contingency/contplan.pdf . The entire Select Committee report is on www.parliament.the-stationery office.co.uk/pa/cm200203/cmselect/cmpubacc/487/48702.htm (visited 8 April 2003).

Reid J. (1968) *Origin of the 1967–68 FMD Epidemic.* Report by the Chief Veterinary Officer, 7 February 1968, Cmnd 3560. London: HMSO. Reproduced in Northumberland (1969a): Appendix 3, 115–117.

Sellers R F. (1968) The inactivation of FMD virus by chemicals and disinfectants. *Veterinary Record* **83**: 504–506.

Sellers R F. (1984) Vesicular viruses, in Wilson G S, Miles A A, Parker M T. (eds) *Topley and Wilson's Principles of Bacteriology, Virology and Immunity.* 7th edn, vol. 4. London: Edward Arnold, 213–232.

Sellers R F, Herniman K A F, Donaldson A I. (1970) Inhalation, persistence and dispersal of FMD virus by man. *Journal of Hygiene* **68**: 565–573.

Skinner H H. (1989) The origins of virus research at Pirbright. *Veterinary History* **6**: 31–40.

Thomson G R. (1996) The role of carrier animals in the transmission of FMD. Sixty-fourth General Session of the Office International des Epizooties. Paris, 20–24 May 1966.

Vallée H, Carre H. (1922) Sur la pluralite du virus aphteux. *Comptes rendus hebdomadaires des seances de l'Academie des Sciences* **174**: 1498–1500.

Vallée H, Carre H, Rinjard P. (1925) On immunization against FMD. *Recueil de Médecine Vétérinaire* **101**: 297–299.

Vallée H, Carre H, Rinjard P. (1926a) Sur l'immunisation anti-aphteuse par le virus formole. *Recueil de Médecine Vétérinaire* **102**: 434–435.

Vallée H, Carre H, Rinjard P. (1926b) Vaccination against FMD by means of formalinized virus. *Journal of Comparative Pathology and Therapeutics* **39**: 326–329.

Whitlock R. (1968) *The Great Cattle Plague: An account of the foot and mouth epidemic of 1967–68.* London: John Baker.

Wilkinson L (1992) *Animals and Disease.* Cambridge: Cambridge University Press.

Woods A. (2002a) *FMD in twentieth century Britain: Science, policy and the veterinary profession.* Unpublished PhD thesis, Manchester University.

Woods A. (2002b) FMD as a weapon of war and its implications for laboratory research in Britain, 1924–1968. *Association of Clinical Pathologists' News* (Spring 2002): 13–17.

Woods A. (2004) The construction of an animal plague: FMD in nineteenth century Britain. *Social History of Medicine* **17**: in press.

Biographical notes

Dr Maurice Allen
DVSc PhD MRCVS FRCPath (b. 1937) was in veterinary practice before joining the staff of the Biochemistry Department at the Central Veterinary Laboratory, Weybridge. He was Head of the Department of Functional Pathology at the Institute for Animal Health, Compton, from 1975 to 1984. Subsequently he established the Compton Paddock Laboratories, which provided diagnostic veterinary services to the veterinary profession and, more recently, milk-testing services for the farming industry. He was involved in the 1967 FMD outbreak at the Crewe centre and in 2001 at Gloucester. He is Past-President of the Association of Veterinary Research Workers and has more than 100 publications, mainly relating to noninfectious diseases in cattle.

Dr John Brooksby
DSc PhD MRCVS was Director of the Animal Virus Research Institute at Pirbright, Surrey, during the FMD outbreak in 1967, until his retirement in 1979.

Miss Mary Brancker
CBE FRCVS (b. 1914), a veterinary surgeon in general practice, was President of the British Veterinary Association (BVA) at the time of the 1967–68 FMD outbreak. She collaborated closely with both MAFF and the National Farmers' Union. Following the outbreak she chaired the BVA committee that gave evidence to the Northumberland Committee.

Professor Leslie Brent
PhD FInstBiol MRCP (b. 1925), a transplantation immunologist, was Professor of Immunology at St Mary's Hospital Medical School from 1969 to 1990, later Emeritus. He co-discovered immunological tolerance in 1953 and graft-versus-host disease in 1957. See Brent L. (1997) *A History of Transplantation Immunology*. San Diego and London: Academic Press.

Professor Fred Brown
OBE FRS (b. 1925) following lectureships at Manchester and Bristol Universities, he joined the Food Preservation Research Station and the Hannah Dairy Research Institute, Ayr, as Senior Scientific Officer in 1950, followed by the Christie Hospital and Holt Radium Institute, Manchester, from 1953 to 1955. He was appointed to the Animal Virus Research Institute, Pirbright, Surrey, as Head of the Biochemistry Department in 1955

and was Deputy Director from 1980 to 1983. He moved to the Wellcome Research Laboratories, Beckenham, Kent, as Head of the Virology Division until 1990 and Professor of Microbiology at the University of Surrey from 1989 to 1990. He has been Adjunct Professor at the School of Epidemiology and Public Health, Yale University, since 1990, and Visiting Scientist at the USDA Plum Island Animal Disease Center, NY, since 1995. He was a member of the Spongiform Encephalopathy Advisory Committee (SEAC) from 1990 to 1998.

Mr Gareth Davies

MRCVS Dip Bact MRCVS DipBact (b. 1935) was Head of the Epidemiology Unit at the Central Veterinary Laboratory, Weybridge, from 1975 to 1986. After a period at Tolworth he became the Veterinary Epidemiologist at the Veterinary Unit of DG6 (Agriculture) at the European Commission. He has been a consultant to the European Commission and the FAO since he retired in 1994, and headed the team that prepared the cost–benefit analysis of vaccination policies for the European Commission in the late 1980s. While in DG6, he dealt with the FMD epidemics in Italy (1993) and Greece (1994) and led a team that recommended an FMD control strategy in Bolivia (1995).

Dr Alex Donaldson

PhD ScD MBE FRSE FRCVS (b. 1942) was Veterinary Research Officer at the Animal Virus Research Institute (the AFRC Institute for Animal Disease Research from 1986 to 1988 and the Institute for Animal Health, Pirbright Lab, since 1988) from 1973, Principal Veterinary Research Officer from 1976 to 1989 and Head of the World Reference Laboratory for FMD at Pirbright from 1985 and has been Head of the Pirbright Laboratory since 1989.

Dr Tony Garland

PhD MRCVS (b. 1938) qualified at the University of Glasgow in 1962 and gained his PhD at the University of London. He worked for the Institute for Animal Health, Pirbright Laboratory, for 17 years from 1962 to 1979, including four years seconded to the Regional Reference Laboratory for FMD in Nairobi, Kenya. At Pirbright he worked in the Departments of Experimental Pathology and Vaccine Research and also in the World Reference Laboratory. He moved to the Wellcome Foundation in 1979 until his retirement in 1997, as Director of Biological Production, including both medical and veterinary vaccines. He had also been based in Brazil in charge of veterinary vaccines research, development and production. Since retirement he has been a consultant for the FAO, the EU and the British Government. He returned to the Pirbright Laboratory in early 2001 during the FMD epidemic for 20 months, including six months as Acting Head of the World Reference Laboratory.

Professor Alan Glynn
FRCP FRCPath (b. 1923) practised clinical medicine at St Mary's Hospital, London, from 1956 to 1958. He took up bacteriology at St Mary's, was appointed Professor in 1971 and Head of the Department of Bacteriology in 1974. In 1980 he became Director of the Central Public Health Laboratory at Colindale until his retirement in 1988.

Sir Ernest Arthur Gowers
GCB KCB CB KBE GBE (1880–1966) entered the Civil Service in 1903 and transferred to the India Office in 1904, becoming a barrister in the Inner Temple in 1906. He served several departments including India, the Chancellor of the Exchequer and the Coal Mines Department. He later became Permanent Under Secretary for Mines, Chairman of the Board of the Inland Revenue, the Coal Mines Reorganization Commission and the Coal Commission until his retirement in 1946. During the Second World War he administered London's civil defence. He chaired many committees, including the Committee on Admission of Women to the Foreign Service, the Royal Commission on Capital Punishment and the Committee on FMD from 1952 to 1953. He wrote three books on the use of English and became editor of *Fowler's Modern English Usage* in 1965.

Mr Sherwin Hall
DHMSA MRCVS (b. 1928) qualified as a veterinary surgeon from the Royal Veterinary College in 1953 and spent five years in farm animal practice before joining MAFF's Veterinary Investigation Service. He worked in the Wolverhampton and Cambridge laboratories and spent two years on a United Nations project in La Paz, Bolivia. In 1977 he was appointed Veterinary Scientific Liaison Officer on the Chief Scientist's Group of MAFF until his retirement in 1988. He founded the Veterinary History Society in 1962.

Sir William MacGregor Henderson
Kt DSc MRCVS FRSE FRS (1913–2000) qualified from the Royal (Dick) Veterinary College, Edinburgh, in 1935, and was on their staff for three years. He joined the staff of the newly formed Animal Virus Research Institute at Pirbright in 1939, and was Deputy

Director in 1955 to 1956. He left in 1957 to become Director of the Pan- American Foot and Mouth Disease Centre, returned to the UK in 1966 as Head of the new Department of Microbiology at the Institute for Research on Animal Diseases at Compton, and was Director from 1967 to 1972, when he became Chief Executive of the Agriculture Research Council until 1978. See Henderson W. (1981) British Agricultural Research and the Agricultural Research Council: a personal historical account, in Cooke G W: (ed.) *Agricultural Research 1931–1981: A history of the Agricultural Research Council and a review of developments in agricultural science during the last 50 years.* London: Agricultural Research Council.

Mr Keith Meldrum

CB MRCVS DVSM HonFRSH (b. 1937) was Chief Veterinary Officer at the MAFF from 1988 until 1997 during the dark days of BSE. He saw FMD in the 1960s as a young veterinary officer in the State Veterinary Service: 'This leads me to feel that a comparison of the two diseases and the control methods that are employed would make a fascinating study for a veterinary historian, but count me out!' Note on draft transcript, 24 October 2002.

The Duke of Montrose

James Graham, 8th Duke of Montrose (b. 1935) has been a livestock farmer since 1962. He was a council member of the National Farmers' Union for Scotland from 1982–90, President of the Strathendrick Agricultural Show since 1966, and President of the Royal Highland and Agricultural Society in 1997–98. He has been Opposition Whip (Conservative) for DEFRA in the House of Lords since 2001.

Mr James Morris

DVSM (b. 1929) was in general veterinary practice in north Wales from 1952 to 1960. He became a veterinary officer with MAFF in Essex from 1960 to 1966 and in Pembrokeshire from 1966 to 1971, before moving to Tolworth as Divisional Veterinary Officer in the import/export section until 1974, and in Kent from 1974 to 1976. He was Deputy Regional Veterinary Officer for the South-West Region from 1976 to 1981 and Regional Veterinary Officer at Tolworth covering meat hygiene and staff officer from 1981 to 1989.

Dr Noel Mowat

PhD MRCVS (b. 1927) trained in veterinary medicine at Glasgow University, was in general veterinary practice and in 1957 joined the staff of the Animal Virus Research

Institute, Pirbright (which merged with the Institute for Research on Animal Diseases (Compton), Houghton Poultry Research Station (Houghton) and the Neuropathogenesis Unit (Edinburgh) to become the Institute for Animal Health from 1988). He has been concerned with the development of vaccines directed to the control of the economically important virus diseases of livestock, principally FMD. He retired as Deputy Director of the Pirbright Laboratory in 1987.

The Duke of Northumberland

Hugh Algernon Percy, 10th Duke of Northumberland G GCVO TD PC JP FRS (1914–88) chaired the Departmental Committee for Recruitment of Veterinary Surgeons in 1964, the Committee of Enquiry on FMD from 1968 to 1969, the Agricultural Research Council from 1958 to 1968 and the Medical Research Council from 1969 to 1977, among others. He was also member of the Agricultural Improvement Council, 1953–62; the National Forestry Committee for England and Wales, 1954–60; the Hill Farming Advisory Committee for England and Wales, 1946–60; the County Agricultural Executive Committee, 1948–59; and the Royal Commission on Historical Manuscripts, 1973–88. He was Chancellor of the University of Newcastle from 1964 to 1988.

Dr Hugh Platt

PhD MRCVS (b. 1921) is a veterinary pathologist with particular interest in the pathogenesis and control of infectious diseases of animals. He was a scientist in the Animal Virus Research Institute, Pirbright, from 1954 to 1967 publishing a number of papers on experimental FMD. From 1967 to 1986 he was Senior Pathologist at the Equine Research Station, Newmarket. His publications include *A Survey of Perinatal Mortality and Disorders in the Thoroughbred* [1979, Newmarket: Animal Health Trust] and an account of a previously unrecognized sexually transmitted disease of horses [Platt H, Taylor C E D. (1982) Contagious equine metritis. *Medical Microbiology* **1**: 49–96].

Dr Walter Plowright

CMG DVSWc FRCVS FRS (b. 1923) qualified from the Royal Veterinary College, London, in 1944. He held posts in the Colonial Veterinary and Research Services from 1951 to 1971, partly on secondment from Pirbright. He was Professor of Veterinary Microbiology and Pathology at the Royal Veterinary College, London, from 1971 to 1978 and Head of the Department of Microbiology,

Institute for Research in Animal Diseases (IRAD, Compton) from 1978 to 1983. He worked in Africa and at Pirbright on many tropical diseases, especially rinderpest (cattle plague), developing a vaccine which has been adopted universally for over 40 years.

Lord Plumb

Henry Plumb DL FRAgS (Lord Plumb of Coleshill from 1987) (b. 1927) farms in Coleshill, Warwickshire. He was elected Vice-President of the National Farmers' Union (NFU) in 1964 and was President from 1970 to 1979. From 1975 to 1977 he was President of Comité des Organizations Professionnelles Agricoles de la CEE (COPA), President of the International Federation of Agricultural Producers (IFAP) from 1977 to 1980, and has been President of the National Federation of Young Farmers' Clubs (NFYFC) from 1976 to 1986 and Deputy President to HRH The Prince of Wales from 2002. He was first elected to the European Parliament (EP) in 1979 and remained a member until his retirement in 1999. He has chaired the European Union Committee of Agriculture (1979–82) and the European Democratic Group (1982–87) and was President of the European Parliament (1987–89), Vice-President of the European People's Party (EPP) from 1994 to 1997, and Co-President of the African, Caribbean and Pacific Countries (ACP)–EU Joint Assembly from 1994 to 1999. His responsibilities included the partnership between the European Union and African, Caribbean and Pacific nations. He was elected Chairman of the Assembly of Former Members of the European Parliament in 2001. See note 100.

Mr Howard Rees

CB DVSM HonFRCVS (b. 1928) qualified at the Royal Veterinary College, London, in 1951, and joined the SVS in 1953. He served as a veterinary officer in Staffordshire from 1953 to 1966 and was involved in numerous outbreaks of FMD in various parts of the country. He was involved in the major outbreak of FMD in 1967–68 and was responsible for the investigation into its origin. He was appointed Chief Veterinary Officer for the SVS in Great Britain in 1980 and retired in 1988. He served as President of the International Animal Health Code Commission of the Office Internationale des Epizooties (OIE) from 1988 to 1997 and as Chairman of the FAO European Commission for the Control of FMD from 1987 to 1989. Following retirement he has been a veterinary consultant on control procedures for FMD to eastern European countries.

Mr John Reid

CB MRCVS DVSM (1906–90) was Regional Veterinary Officer in 1958 and Chief Veterinary Officer, Ministry of Agriculture, Fisheries and Food from 1965 to 1970. He was Vice Chairman of the European Commission for the Control of FMD from 1967 to 1970 and a member of the Committee of Inquiry into the Veterinary Profession from 1971 to 1975.

Mr Alan Richardson

PhD MRCVS (b. 1940) was in large animal veterinary practice for three years before being appointed to the MAFF's State Veterinary Service. He was a Veterinary Investigation Officer (VIO) based at Penrith in Cumberland in 1967. Being judged to be a competent diagnostician by the Officer in Charge at the Macclesfield FMD centre, the late Mr John Loxham, he was included in a team responsible for second opinions and awkward cases. Later, he was Director of the Sir William McDonald Veterinary Laboratory, Victoria, Australia from 1975 to 1976; veterinary clinical research manager with ICI Pharmaceuticals Ltd., Macclesfield, from 1977 to 1985; and a Home Office Inspector from 1987 to 1996.

Professor David Rowlands

PhD (b. 1940) was a member of staff at the Animal Virus Research Institute, Pirbright, researching FMD virus from 1964 to 1983. Subsequently he was head of FMD virus research at Wellcome Biotech, Pirbright, working principally on new approaches to vaccination against FMD. He has been Professor of Molecular Virology, University of Leeds, since 1996.

Mr Chris Schermbrucker

DTVM MIBiol QP MRCVS (b. 1935) a veterinary surgeon, trained in the development of vaccines against FMD at Wellcome, Pirbright, from 1966 to 1967. He led a joint-venture team producing successful African-strain vaccines in Nairobi for 14 years, returning to Pirbright in 1980, where he set up modern quality-control systems at the foot and mouth laboratory there and at related laboratories overseas. He is recognized as a Qualified Person under the EU directive and has been consulted by the UK and many overseas governments on the practicalities for the control and eradication of FMD. He retired from the Vaccine Production Lab at Pirbright in 2000.

Mr Jim Scudamore

MRCVS (b. 1944) was DVO, later Veterinary Research Officer in Kenya from 1968 to 1974, joining MAFF (DEFRA from 2001) in 1974 as a Veterinary Investigation Officer, rising to DVO at Tolworth from 1980 to 1994 as well as DVO in Taunton from 1984 to 1987, and RVO in Edinburgh from 1987 to 1990, later Assistant Chief Veterinary Officer, Edinburgh until 1996. He served as Assistant Chief Veterinary Officer (meat hygiene) at Tolworth in 1996–97 and has been Chief Veterinary Officer since 1997 and Director General of Animal Health and Welfare from 2001.

Dr Bob Sellers

PhD ScD MRCVS FRSE (b. 1924), a veterinary virologist, worked on FMD and other vesicular virus diseases (tissue culture, vaccines and interferon, diagnosis and disease control, and spread of virus by the airborne route) and on bluetongue at Pirbright from 1953 to 1958 and from 1964 to 1979 as Deputy Director and as Director from 1979 to 1984. He also worked at the Wellcome Research Laboratories, Beckenham, from 1958 to 1962 on canine distemper and hepatitis vaccines, and on interferon. In Venezuela from 1962 to 1964 he worked on FMD and Venezuelan equine encephalitis and in Canada from 1985 to 1988 as a consultant on foreign animal disease. In 2001–02 he was a member of the Royal Society of Edinburgh Inquiry into FMD in Scotland. At the beginning of the 2001 outbreak he prepared two documents for friends and family, 'Ruminations on FMD' (BFMD1a) and 'Vaccination, treatment or slaughter or a combination' (BFMD2), which will be deposited with the records of this meeting in the Archives and Manuscripts, Wellcome Library, London.

Lord Soulsby

Ernest Jackson Lawson Soulsby PhD MRCVS DVSM (Baron Soulsby of Swaffham Prior from 1990) (b. 1926), was a graduate of the Royal (Dick) School of Veterinary Studies, Edinburgh, in 1948, with honorary degrees from several universities and has served as President of the Royal College of Veterinary Surgeons from 1984 to 1985, and of the Royal Society of Medicine from 1999 to 2000. He spent 15 years as Head of the Department of Pathobiology at the University of Pennsylvania, USA, and from 1978 to 1993 was Professor of Animal Pathology at the University of Cambridge and Dean of the Veterinary Faculty from 1978 to 1992. His major research and veterinary interests have been the immunology of parasitic infections, the parasitic zoonoses and livestock research and development in developing countries, having been an adviser and consultant to national and international organizations and governments.

Dr Tilli Tansey
PhD PhD HonMRCP (b. 1953) is Convenor of the History of Twentieth Century Medicine Group and Reader in the History of Modern Medical Sciences at the Wellcome Trust Centre for the History of Medicine at University College London.

Mr Angus Taylor
MRCVS (b. 1917) qualified as a veterinary surgeon in Edinburgh in 1941. After two years as an assistant in practice, he joined the Ministry of Agriculture and Fisheries in 1943. He became the Divisional Veterinary Officer for Cheshire and set up the first Foot and Mouth Centre in the country at Crewe in 1967. It was the 17th outbreak of FMD in which he had worked since 1944. He was a technical adviser to the BVA when evidence was prepared for the Northumberland Committee, and gave evidence on behalf of the Association of State Veterinary Officers. He was Regional Veterinary Officer at Cambridge from 1971 until 1982, and President of the British Veterinary Association from 1972 to 1973 and of the Royal College of Veterinary Surgeons from 1982 to 1983.

Mr Ken Tyrrell
MRCVS (b. 1929) qualified in veterinary medicine at Trinity College Dublin in 1951 and joined the Ministry of Agriculture and Fisheries in 1953, where he worked until his retirement in 1987. He was first involved in FMD control in Torrington, Devon, in August 1953, later Askerswell, Dorset; Blandford, Sturminster Newton, Marlborough, Yeovil, Liskeard, Downham Market, Rothbury and Nantwich. In 1967/68, he diagnosed the first case of FMD in Cheshire on 30 October 1967 and the last case in 1968. He was seconded as a consultant on FMD to the Food and Agriculture Organization of the United Nations in Turkey, and to the Pirbright Research Institute on vaccination trials in Namibia in 1962. He examined Charolais cattle for FMD in France prior to the first importation of this breed into the UK and Simmental cattle in Switzerland in 1965.

Professor Sir William Weipers
Kt FRCVS DVSM FRSE (1904–90) was in general veterinary practice for 24 years before becoming the Director of Veterinary Education at the University of Glasgow in 1949 and Dean of the Faculty of Veterinary Medicine from 1968 until his retirement in 1974. He was a member of the Council of

Royal College of Veterinary Surgeons from 1949 to 1974 and President during 1963–64, and a member of the Northumberland Committee from 1969 to 1969.

Dr Abigail Woods
PhD MRCVS (b. 1972) worked in general veterinary practice for two years before studying the history of science, technology and medicine at the University of Manchester. In 2002 she completed a Wellcome Trust-funded PhD thesis entitled 'FMD in twentieth-century Britain: Science, policy and the veterinary profession'.

Glossary

AI
Artificial insemination.

Animal Health Act 2002
Received the Royal Assent on 7 November 2002. The provisions strengthen existing controls and introduce new powers to include other animal diseases. A national contingency plan and an annual report on import controls are to be published, as well as details of illegal imports of animal products. Rigorous and detailed conditions must be met before a warrant is granted to enter a farm and permit the slaughter of contiguous livestock. The Secretary of State has a duty to consider whether vaccination is appropriate. See DEFRA news release 455/02, 8 November 2002, at www.defra.gov.uk/news/2002/ (visited 25 November 2002).

Animal Health Group
MAFF's traditional civil service generalist administrators were located at Tolworth (along with the SVS), whose undersecretary (Grade 3 head) was based in London until mid-1992. Its responsibility covered policy development for animal health, welfare and breeding, meat hygiene, exports and imports of animals, meat and meat products; and licensing, distribution and control of veterinary medicines until the Veterinary Medicines Directorate was set up in 1989. It was also responsible for implementing many aspects of these policies.

Blanket vaccination
Vaccination of all animals within a defined area.

BSE
Bovine Spongiform Encephalopathy.

BVA
British Veterinary Association.

Capsid
The outer protein coat of a virus, enclosing the nucleic acid. See Figure 10.

Complement fixation test
One of the first laboratory methods used for the identification of a virus serotype or the presence of FMD antibodies in an infected animal. It is based on the fact that complement – a normal constituent of serum – is bound or 'fixed' when antigen and antibody that are specifically related, interact or combine. The test is carried out in two stages: (1) antigen, complement (usually guinea-pig serum complement) and serum which has been inactivated by heating, are incubated together.

(2) When this reaction is complete, an indicator component prepared from sheep erythrocytes sensitized with antisheep red blood cell antibody is added. If complement remains from the first stage, the sensitized red blood cells will lyse. If no lysis occurs the antigen and antibody are serologically related. Knowing the serotype of either the antigen or the antiserum makes it possible to identify the other component. A result is obtained in three hours if sufficient antigen is present in the sample. Assay methods to measure (titrate) the amount of either component were developed and the serum-virus neutralization test was also introduced to assess the antibody levels in animals which had either been infected in the field or had been immunized by vaccination. Both these methods have now been largely superseded by the enzyme-linked immunosorbent assay (ELISA) test – which offers significant practical advantages over the earlier tests. Additional information from Dr Noel Mowat and Dr Bob Sellers.

Contiguous

Land next to an infected farm with livestock and if livestock were in the field adjacent to the affected stock on the **IP**, then they might be slaughtered as 'dangerous contacts'. The term was not used to mean all livestock within two miles (3 km) as in 2001.

CLA

County Landowners Association.

CVO

Chief Veterinary Officer.

DEFRA

Department for Environment, Food and Rural Affairs took over the functions of the **Ministry of Agriculture, Fisheries and Food in** June 2001.

DVO

Divisional Veterinary Officer, usually responsible for one English county.

DVSc

Doctor of Veterinary Science.

EC/EU

European Commission/European Union.

EC cost–benefit analyses

'The Commission of the EC, seeking a harmonized policy for FMD when the single market was due to come into operation after 1992, had undertaken cost–benefit analyses for two possible strategies: either nonvaccination or pan-Europe vaccination. The results were interpreted to mean that the overall economic benefits would be greater if prophylactic vaccination would be stopped. They concluded this having considered that the worst possible future outbreak scenario could be something like 13 primary outbreaks and 150 secondaries during a ten-year period. (Of course the recent UK outbreak shows this to have been far too optimistic, however it is the historical case.) The case for cessation of vaccination was also considered to have an advantage due to the EC regulations for the movement of animals and animal products at the time.' Additional information from Mr Chris Schermbrucker. See notes 30 and 62. See also **Vaccination in EC**.

FAO
Food and Agriculture Organization of the United Nations.

FMC
The Fatstock Marketing Corporation (FMC) was set up in 1954 by the **National Farmers' Union** (NFU). Capital was raised by subscription from members. FMC became a public company in 1962 and bought Marsh and Baxter Ltd. By that time the business had more than 10 500 employees. Hillsdown Holdings bought the FMC meat processing and slaughterhouse business in 1984, and later sold its abattoirs, eventually ceasing red meat production. See also NFU.

FMD
Foot and mouth disease.

FMD vaccine
The first experimental FMD vaccines were prepared in 1925 by Vallée and his colleagues using formaldehyde-inactivated vesicular fluid from infected calves. It soon became clear that a method for the large-scale production of virus *in vitro* would be required for the extensive application of a vaccine in control programmes. H S Frenkel in Holland developed the first industrial method by collecting the tongue epithelial tissues from healthy cattle at local abattoirs and producing the virus in quantity in large sterilizable vessels. The virus was inactivated with formalin, and aluminium hydroxide was added as an adjuvant. This vaccine was effective in the early national control programmes, but there were some disadvantages. In some batches, virus inactivation was not totally complete, resulting in a low level of infectivity that could initiate outbreaks of the disease.' Additional information from Dr Noel Mowat.

Form C
An order enforcing an emergency standstill (under the FMD Order) or stop on all movements of susceptible animals within a limited area (5 miles). When the disease was confirmed the area was extended to

cover about a ten-miles radius from the infected premises.

Foyer
Siège principal d'une maladie, or main source of the disease. See page 46.

GSOII
Royal Army Veterinary Corps (RAVC) General Staff Officer Grade II.

HEPA
High efficiency particle abstractions filter, effective for virus control.

Immunogenic
Some antigens stimulate a better immune response than others and are described as highly immunogenic.

IP
Infected premises or 'infected area' as defined by the Foot and Mouth Disease (Infected Areas Restrictions) Order of 1938.

International Vaccine Bank
It was established at the Institute for Animal Health, **Pirbright**, Surrey, in 1985, which also held the World Reference Laboratory for FMD for the Food and Agriculture Organization of the United Nations (**FAO**) from 1958 and the Office Internationale des Epizooties (**OIE**) from 1960, and the EC Reference Laboratory for FMD from 1985 to 1995. See also Forman and Garland (2002).

Lairage
An area of a slaughterhouse where animals are rested, fed and watered prior to slaughter.

LVI
Local Veterinary Inspector.

MAFF
Ministry of Agriculture, Fisheries and Food, formerly Ministry of Agriculture and Food , which has been **DEFRA** since 2001.

NCO
Non-commissioned officer.

NFU
The National Farmers' Union was started by a group of nine Lincolnshire countrymen in 1904. See www.nfu.org.uk/ (visited 21 November 2002). NFU archives, including files from the **Fatstock Marketing Corporation** (SR 2NFU SP1/1–4), are held by the Rural History Centre, University of Reading. See archive listing at www.rdg.ac.uk/Instits/im/rural/archsr.html (visited 25 June 2003).

NUAW
National Union of Agricultural Workers.

ODA
Overseas Development Administration.

OIE

Office Internationale des Epizooties with 158 member countries sets sanitary rules for international trade in animals and animal products, and disseminates veterinary scientific information on animal disease control.

Pirbright

The Animal Virus Research Institute at Pirbright, Surrey, was a grant-aided Institute under the Agricultural Research Council (later Agricultural and Food Research Council). Diagnosis and research before 1964 was primarily devoted to FMD, but later expanded to include many other exotic virus diseases. See Skinner (1989). In 1986 the Institute for Animal Disease Research was formed by the amalgamation of the Institute for Research in Animal Diseases (IRAD) at Compton, Berkshire, the Animal Virus Research Institute at Pirbright, the Houghton Poultry Research Station, at Houghton, Cambridgeshire (closed in 1993) and the ARC/MRC Neuropathogenesis Unit in Edinburgh. The name was changed two years later to the Institute for Animal Health (IAH), administered from Compton. An extract from the Biotechnology and Biological Sciences Research Council (BBSRC) paper in June 1988 summarized the Council's position towards Pirbright: 'The conclusion... was that IAH should be consolidated on a single site at Compton within five years. However, there were a number of constraints limiting Council's ability to achieve this scientifically desirable objective. Because of the need for high security disease containment for some of the work on exotic virus diseases, it would be necessary to retain a centre for the diagnosis and control of foot and mouth and other exotic diseases at Pirbright.' E-mail to Mrs Lois Reynolds from Allan Black, BBSRC Council Secretariat, 14 July 2003. Additional information from Dr Bob Sellers.

Plum Island Animal Disease Center

The United States Department of Agriculture (USDA) research centre is located on Plum Island, off the north-eastern tip of Long Island, and is part of the town of Southold, in Suffolk County, New York, USA, with an area of 840 acres (1.3 square miles).
See www.ars.usda.gov/plum/index.html (visited 24 June 2003).

Primary outbreak

One with no established connection with a known outbreak in Britain, therefore from a foreign source.

RASE
Royal Agricultural Society of England.

RAVC
Royal Army Veterinary Corps.

RVO
The Regional Veterinary Officer headed one of **MAFF**'s seven English centres [with separate organizations in the Welsh Department and Scottish Office] in 1967 with close collaboration with MAFF administrators at divisional level located in the same premises. By 2001, the regional structure had been amalgamated into three regions, while the National Assembly for Wales and the Scottish Executive had become separate bodies, as was the Institute for Animal Health [funded by a core grant from the Biotechology and Biological Sciences Research Council and from contracts from MAFF]; the Veterinary Laboratories Agency [an executive agency of the Department for Environment, Food and Rural Affairs (**DEFRA**) from 1990, which provided vets and scientific advisers; loaned staff to **Pirbright** as well as equipment, protective clothing, firearms and ammunition; and developed risk assessments; coordinated sero-surveillance and testing at its Penrith, Luddington and Shewsbury laboratories]; the Met Office [a trading fund of the Ministry of Defence] and the Rural Payments Agency [formerly the Intervention Board, a MAFF executive agency, which administered and organized disposal of carcasses].

Ring vaccination
A method of controlling the spread of infections that involves vaccinating susceptible animals in a circle around outbreaks. An economic assessment of costs prepared for the Northumberland Committee in 1968 suggested that vaccination in an area of five to ten miles around an outbreak could take seven to ten days to complete, with a further 14 days for full immunity to develop. Each vaccination ring would cover an area of 50 000 acres, enclosing average livestock numbers of 12 500 cattle, 22 500 sheep and 7500 pigs at a total cost of 21¼p per dose for cattle; 9½p for sheep and 31½p per dose for pigs. See 'An economic assessment of alternative control policies for FMD in Great Britain', MAFF/CI/12 for NC(MAFF)(68)13, Appendix 9, 1.

RSPCA
Royal Society for the Prevention of Cruelty to Animals.

Secondary outbreak
One that comes from established infections in Britain.

Slaughterhouse

The Northumberland Report distinguished between 'slaughterhouses' and 'knacker's yards': the former were constructed to a high standard of disease security, the latter operated to a lower standard of hygiene and were licensed. The Meat (Sterilization) Regulations 1969 covering England and Wales required all meat and offal unfit for human consumption and all knacker meat to be sterilized before sale. See Northumberland (1969b): 42–43, paras 85–87.

Standstill order

Form C (under an FMD Order) enforced a standstill or cessation of all movement of susceptible animals within five miles of premises where disease was suspected to be present. When the disease was confirmed an extended area covered about ten miles radius from the **infected premises** ('infected area') as defined by the Foot and Mouth Disease (Infected Areas Restrictions) Order of 1938.

State Veterinary Service

In 1967 the State Veterinary Service (SVS) of qualified veterinary staff, headed by the Chief Veterinary Officer (**CVO**), was part of **MAFF**'s Agricultural Development and Advisory Service (ADAS). It became a separate service in 1987, managed by the CVO, who retained a line management link to the Director-General of ADAS. Between 1990 to 1994 this link ceased when the SVS became part of MAFF's Animal Health and Veterinary Group (AHVG), created by the merger of the Animal Health Group and the SVS. The SVS is now an agency within Great Britain responsible for animal health matters, including notifiable disease outbreaks, the control of which involves slaughter and burial, or incineration, of carcasses on farms, together with disinfection of buildings and equipment. Their official journal, the *State Veterinary Journal*, covers disease control, animal welfare, public health and consumer protection.

Susceptible animals

For FMD these are defined as cloven-hoofed animals, such as cattle, sheep, pigs and goats.

SVD

Swine vesicular disease.

Tolworth

Headquarters of the **State Veterinary Service** in Tolworth, Surrey, from 1945 to 2001.
The Animal Health Group was also located at Tolworth (although its Grade 3 head was based in London until mid-1992) and was responsible for developing policy on animal health, welfare and breeding; meat hygiene; exports and imports of

animals, meat and meat products; and (until the Veterinary Medicines Directorate was set up in 1989 as a separate unit) on the licensing, distribution and control of veterinary medicines. It was also responsible for implementing many aspects of these policies.

TVI
Temporary Veterinary Inspector.

Vaccination in EC
Mr Chris Schermbrucker wrote: 'The proposal by the Commission to the Council of Ministers was made on 26 June 1990 in the form of Directive 90/423/EEC. Article 4 required the completion of the arrangements to set up a bank of FMD vaccines for emergency use, and revision of control measures for the importation of animals and animal products from third countries. Member countries would cease vaccination against FMD by 1 January 1992 and on the same date prohibit the importation of vaccinated animals into their territory.' Additional information from Mr Chris Schermbrucker.

Vaccine Bank
See International Vaccine Bank.

WRVS
Women's Royal Voluntary Services.

Index: Subject

Index: Names

Biographical notes appear in bold